By Julius Horwitz

The W.A.S.P.

Julius Horwitz

The
W.A.S.P.

NEW YORK 1967 *Atheneum*

I wish to express my gratitude to the Guggenheim Foundation
for their kind and generous assistance

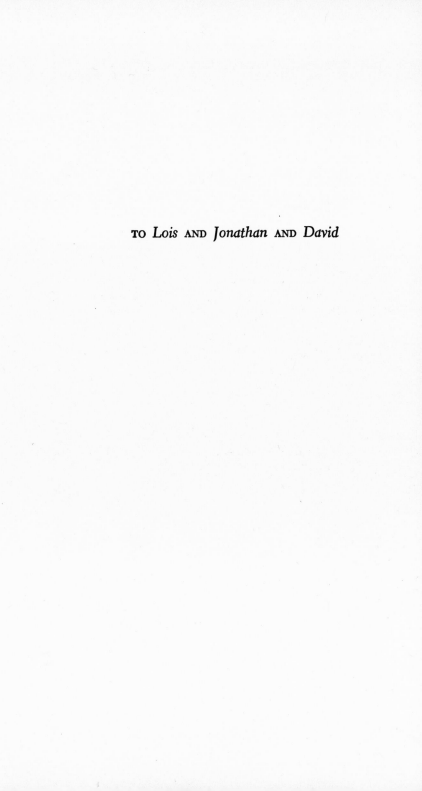

TO *Lois* AND *Jonathan* AND *David*

THE CHAPEL

ALL THAT remained was to bury S. T. West and to find out why he had died. I passed his body in the funeral parlor on Madison Avenue and saw that he no longer existed. The undertakers do a magnificent job of erasing the last traces of life. I took a seat midway up the chapel on the aisle and looked for familiar faces. Only the funerals of the celebrated attract large crowds in New York. A man like West could not reasonably expect all of his friends and acquaintances to attend his funeral. How many funerals did he attend? Death doesn't exist in Manhattan. It is one of the wonders of Manhattan that it has obliterated death. Here and there, at Trinity Church and other hallowed pieces of ground there are the dead, but they have been there for so long that they seem like one of us. On upper Broadway there is a large cemetery, but it is filled with old-fashioned vaults that look as if the family papers were buried in them and not bodies that once settled the island. The people West knew were the busy people of New York. Death had no meaning for them. They couldn't even conceive of death. The *New York Times* obituary page had taken away from them the terror of death. They lived to be busy and they would die like the automobiles thrown on the junk pile facing the Harlem River at 207th Street.

Here and there in the chapel I began to make out faces and I nodded hello. In the front two rows sat West's family. They formed a solid aisle of silence and they sat stiffly, neither whispering nor glancing. They were dutiful toward death. They knew it was a bill that you had to pay. They behaved as though they had invented it. There was a rumor in the chapel as I entered it that West was going to be treated as a martyr in the eulogy. The newspapers hadn't let West's death go unnoticed. The murder of the aged couple, Mr. and Mrs. Reid, and the two boys who committed the murders were forgotten in the coverage given to West's journey into Harlem to offer his legal services to the families of the two murderers. Such things don't go unnoticed in the New York papers. But not enough had been made of the story to give West lasting newspaper fame as a martyr, to make it impossible for anyone who daily read the papers to ever forget his name. This is the quality of fame: never to forget a man's name, no matter what he did or didn't do. I looked for Jenny Beal in the chapel, but I didn't see her. She was supposed to fly in from Alabama. Nor did I see Emerson, whom I expected to see as soon as I entered the chapel. I did see the drug addict who had spoken so eloquently in West's living room the second time I met Emerson. I saw Charles Eaton enter and take a seat in the rear. He didn't notice me. The chapel was now rapidly filling up as though the mourners were arriving by taxi, hopping out, before the eulogy began. I weep at funerals, and I hoped the minister would be able to make me weep at the death of West. There was certainly enough to weep about. I like to think that funerals are great symphonies. The mind soars at them, nothing can intrude between the knowledge that death is real and the mind attempting to find out what the reality is. Here we are even more naked than we are before our wives. There are, God save us, moments in existence that belong to us beyond what money can buy or we would care to buy. We are extraordinary, to use Emerson's word, even though we seem to be running through civilizations trying to prove the contrary. Perhaps the most extraordinary achievement of man was learning how to carve himself with a velvety smoothness out of marble.

The chapel was now almost filled, and the black-suited ushers who moved so much like shadows were quietly setting up folding chairs. There was a restlessness in the chapel, for no one had appeared to take charge of the services. West had been a very prominent Protestant layman, as they said in the obituaries. He believed in God. Lately there were preachers who were saying "God is dead" as though their saying it made a difference.

I suspected that if West had known he was going to die he might have prepared his own eulogy, the kind of presentation on justice he always wanted to deliver in court. There was no way now of knowing how he felt about the irony of his death. I was sure he had wanted to live to be a ripe old man and finally escape from life by

5

having his memory dim and then extinguish like a candle burnt to the end, with nothing remaining except its pervasive glow.

I looked again for Emerson in the chapel, but didn't see him. I hadn't been able to get hold of Emerson after West died. The phone didn't answer at the church, and when I went there the doors were closed. I walked the six flights up to Emerson's apartment in Harlem, but he wasn't home and none of the neighbors on the top floor had seen him. I slipped a note under his door asking him to call me. The super of Emerson's building told me that Emerson had not moved. In a burst of sentimental persuasion I thought Emerson had gone off like a wounded animal.

The rustling in the chapel grew louder and I half expected to hear a hand-clapping start, as though to hurry the proceedings. I had now absorbed most of the faces in the chapel and they were the people whose decisions affected the lives of millions of people who weren't able to make decisions for themselves. I suspected they were attracted to West's funeral because he had died in the field as they died daily at their desks.

A door opened near the pulpit and a minister appeared, a tall, lean minister whom I remembered meeting at a party with S. T. West. There was an immediate silence. The minister didn't glance at the mourners, for he probably doubted their capacity to mourn. He walked directly to the pulpit, opened a book, closed it, opened it again and then read, " 'No, no, no, no! Come, let's away to prison; we two alone will sing like birds i' the cage:

6

When thou dost ask me blessing, I'll kneel down, And ask of thee forgiveness: and we'll live, and pray, and sing, and tell old tales and laugh at gilded butterflies, and hear poor rogues talk of court news; and we'll talk with them too, who loses, and who wins; who's in, who's out; and take upon's the mystery of things, as if we were God's spies; and we'll wear out, in a wall'd prison, packs and sets of great ones that ebb and flow by the moon.'"

There was a hum of recognition of the Shakespeare as the minister paused, a hum of recognition that was almost a sigh of relief, for S. T. West wasn't going to be buried like a dead man, a cold waxed dead man irrevocably dead; no, he was going to be buried without a reminder of death, the hum seemed to say.

"This," said the minister, "was S. T. West's favorite passage in all literature. And, I think, of a lot of other intelligent people who know they will never be listened to, not in the voice they choose to speak, and they find comfort in Shakespeare's words for the little comfort the words can give. King Lear was never able to go off to his wall'd prison. He wasn't permitted to live. To live is everything. It is in life that we can speak to one another. However we honor death, we ought to honor life more.

"In the week before Sam West died, we sat together in his office with all of his papers pushed aside. For a year he had had a premonition of his death. In a way which he couldn't satisfactorily explain to himself or to me—and he was an expert at finding explanations—he thought that a murder would occur which in some way would lay clear, like the Salk vaccine, a positive way of dealing with

7

crime and deprivation in our world. He was not so simple-minded as to think that crime could be erased or depriva-tion cease, but he did think that practical solutions ex-isted if only we wanted to make them practical. We sat in his law office and talked about death. But since we were both ignorant of death, what we were really talking about was life. In the course of the conversation West asked me if I would do him a favor. I said I would. He then said—without being melodramatic but like a lawyer advising a client on his will, West said to me, If I should die before you do, then you would be the most likely per-son to speak at my services. If that happens, then I would like you to ask Thomas Emerson to speak."

The silence in the chapel was broken by a stirring, a loud rising of voices which, if the people sitting next to me set an example, meant that Emerson was being iden-tified. The minister, John Holmes Marsh, waited until the voices were aware they were in a chapel, and in an instant the stirring ended. The minister looked toward the crowded pews where the mourners now sat hunched forward like the Friday-night spectators at Madison Square Garden. West the courtroom lawyer, the trial lawyer, the man who spoke to the mercy of juries, who sought evidence in human contacts, had now shifted the funeral to himself, a courtroom manipulation that would have brought smiles from a judge smarter than the law permitted him to be.

All that remained was to find out why West had died.

I could feel myself hunching forward as the minister, John Holmes Marsh, left the pulpit and Emerson entered the chapel.

Emerson wore a black suit. Not one of the black suits West had given him, but a new suit, so it seemed as the light from the stained-glass windows fell on him. He didn't look toward the crowded pews. He did look up for an instant at the stained-glass windows lit by the late morning sun. Emerson's face looked as though he had been weeping for days. There were lines under his eyes. His shoulders drooped. His lean body looked soft, as though it had been pounded by boulders. His hands were tense, his long fingers opening and closing, closing on themselves, seizing his thoughts. He could read nothing from the mourners in front of him. Nor from the two rows of West's family. Who could know what family arguments went on in Boston, Philadelphia, New York, Short Hills, Chevy Chase when they heard, if they heard, that a black man, almost an unfrocked minister, almost twenty years younger than S. T. West, was going to speak at the death of a member of the family? West's family extended throughout the Eastern seaboard like a chain of supermarkets. Of all the members, West was the most public, for it was a family that felt its strength in obscurity. Now they sat before his dead body and even in death West had to remind them that they could no longer pretend that the new America didn't exist. Maybe Emerson would talk to this point. Maybe not. I couldn't anticipate for an instant what Emerson was going to say, and I waited for his words, as he waited for them, in the moment of silence before he began to speak.

I saw Emerson's lips open and the words took shape.

"First let me say that I am not astonished by death. I have been more dead than alive most of my life. And like most of the people of my race, I have often found death, to be dead, more a way of experiencing life than life itself." Emerson spoke with authority. As the words came out of him, they were shaped by events he would probably spend the rest of his life trying to grasp.

"Let me recount for you the way S. T. West died. On September 6 in the early afternoon, S. T. West pushed the elevator button on the fifteenth floor of his apartment building. Within seconds the elevator ascended, and as he opened the door he saw two bodies. Both battered, both dead. They were the bodies of two aged tenants in the building, Mr. and Mrs. Reid. They had been beaten to death with an iron rod that lay on the floor of the elevator. West telephoned for the police. Within minutes of telephoning the police, a patrolman on West 93rd Street noticed two young boys walking toward the subway entrance, their clothes splattered with blood and blood still on their hands and faces. They told the police officer that they had been involved in a street fight and they were on their way home to West 118th Street to wash up and change their clothes. It sounded reasonable, considering the character of the West Nineties area of upper Broadway. But the police officer was suspicious. He said to the two boys, Let's take a walk up the block. The police officer was within his rights because the two boys did present a suspicious picture, despite their age. It is no secret that today half of the major crimes in America are committed by children under the

age of eighteen. As they walked up the block, they heard
police sirens and saw police cars stopping at the apartment building where the aged couple was murdered and
where S. T. West lived. Within minutes it was clearly
established by the police that the two boys had beaten
the aged couple with an iron bar, had taken a wallet with
seventy-six dollars in it and had ripped a diamond wed-
ding ring off the finger of the old woman. One of the two
boys was wearing an Omega wrist watch with the initials
of the dead lawyer. West was present at the investigation
that swiftly linked the two boys to the murder, even
though there were no witnesses to the murder.

"It was not the first time S. T. West had been present
at murder. For eleven years West had defended, without fee, youths in Harlem and East Harlem who were
arrested on charges of murder. But this was the first
time he had seen the victims while their bodies were still
warm with death, and the first time that he was absolutely certain of the identity of the murderers. Here was a
murder with all present. The victims, the young murderers, the attorney, the police, all staring into the elevator car, its walls covered with blood, its floor that would
from that day hold trembling feet as the white passengers rode up alongside black passengers, the white passengers wondering if it was their turn to be murdered
or robbed.

"West had no choice. He had to find out who the boys
were, what their families were like, what events had led
up to the murders, what in the background of the two
boys had led them to effortlessly murder an aged couple.

We know that he sat for about an hour in his apartment pondering the murder, and that he had an appointment to meet a friend at a spot that he had particularly chosen to discuss the double murder, the sixty-fifth floor of the RCA Building, where, if the sky is clear, you can look down on this unimaginable city and see it all come together as though it had meaning or purpose. But West didn't keep his appointment. Instead, he went by taxi to Harlem, to West 118th Street, where the two young murderers lived in the same building. West first went to the apartment of Mrs. Mills, the mother of the younger of the two. When Mrs. Mills came to the door and S. T. West told her that her son had finally committed murder, a murder which she had been expecting him to commit, she screamed, and it was the depth of her screams, the terror of her screams, the hopelessness of her screams, the finality of her screams, that bounded against West. The screams bombarded his soul and they struck him dead, for he was not able to silence the screams. His heart convulsed into a terrible knot, squeezed itself into an irrevocable knot and cut off his life. He died as Mrs. Mills' screams were still bombarding his already dead body. With his death, the rest is conjecture about West."

Emerson paused, but no one in the chapel moved, not even to glance at one another.

"Why was it this murder that killed S. T. West and not the eighty-five hundred other murders that are committed each year? Why did West want to die at this point in his life, at the age of forty-seven, with perhaps thirty more years of life possible to him, thirty years to roll back the darkness? For if he had kept his appointment on the sixty-fifth floor, or if he had merely stayed in his apartment, he would not be dead.

"For the past two years I have known S. T. West. In a way that I won't forget, he rescued me from banality. Though we never truly understood each other, that was our understanding. When I learned of the circumstances of his death, I decided to go back to the same door, to Mrs. Mills, to knock on her door and to do what West had wanted to do. I wanted to find out who and what these boys, age fourteen and fifteen, were, who had committed the double murder and now this third murder, West's. For if a man is killed before he completes his work, he is murdered.

"Mrs. Mills admitted me to her apartment. It's not an apartment, really; it's in one of those abandoned filthy buildings in Harlem where, for want of any other living space, about five hundred thousand black Americans live and produce the children who now haunt American life. There is no mystery about this. These buildings and these children and these mothers have been known to all the agencies of government in this city for the past twenty years.

"Mrs. Mills has three rooms. One for eating, a living room that is also used as a bedroom, and a bedroom with two bunk beds. She has five children. She is unwed, as they say in the social-welfare journals. She had four different fathers for her five children. The oldest of her children is Ralph Mills, age fourteen, the murderer. The case history of Mrs. Mills has become a stereotype in American life, but it is a stereotype that is haunting the highest levels of government in Washington. But worse, she is an object of study, which means she is an object of doom. Just a few years ago her existence was denied by those who defended the public-welfare world as the best of possible worlds for the worst possible people in American life. Today she is the object of confidential reports written by the Department of Labor, she is the object of speeches delivered by the President of the United States and she has given employment to a vast new industry, the industry of poverty, while her own poverty remains untouched and her children die daily in their welfare bunk beds.

"The father of Ralph Mills was named George Thomas. He came to New York from Alabama sixteen years ago. He started living with Mrs. Mills, and he worked as a garage handyman, hoping to achieve the title of mechanic, but Mrs. Mills became pregnant and he resorted to the black man's divorce. He left Mrs. Mills to the mercy of the welfare system and she never saw him again. Mrs. Mills moved into the building on West 118th Street after being shunted by the Department of Welfare from one filthy building to another, each worse than the other, and she was never able to find an apartment with more than one room. When she found the apartment on West 118th Street with three rooms she thought she had achieved paradise. The first night she and her two children had to sleep on the floor because the Department of Welfare had not yet made money

14

available to her to buy furniture. She slept with her children on the floor for a week before she received enough money to buy a bed, bunk beds, a table, three chairs and blankets. The first night on the floor she saw the rats come out of the walls, not mice but rats, and she stayed awake beating off the rats, which smelled the young flesh of her children, for the rats in Harlem have developed a decided taste for the flesh of young children. The second night she went to the superintendent of her building and asked him to nail tin plates over the rat holes. None of this is an excuse for murder. It is a cause for murder.

"Mrs. Mills told me that within six months she was horrified of the building and what went on in it but she didn't know where to move. She saw children of eight and ten addicted to narcotics. She saw boys of eleven taking down their pants for homosexuals in the hallways, she saw girls of ten and twelve licking men on the roof, for which they earned from twenty cents to a dollar. She saw children sleeping in the halls while their mothers entertained on the only bed in the room. She saw girls of thirteen and fourteen grow pregnant, and on the roof she would sometimes see a baby not yet born but forever dead. She saw children blindly skilled in the administration of heroin who couldn't read three sentences in their native language, English. She told me that her baby, Ralph, was young, just an infant then, he wouldn't see these things. Somehow, in a perverse way which we are just beginning to understand, Mrs. Mills felt at home in the building, because, in the famous phrase of a friend of mine, she lived in an expectancy of failure and the building made her realize her expectations of failure. In these terms her life was a success. But of course the infant, the three-year-old, saw what was going on. By the time he was three years old he had seen more filth than perhaps eighty percent of the people in this chapel will ever see, even though most of the people here today are concerned professionally with this filth. At the age of five he was homosexually assaulted by a drunk who forced his penis into his mouth and Ralph Mills had to be hospitalized for a week for observation and treatment because the drunk who homosexually assaulted him had syphilis. At the age of seven he was raped by two boys on the roof. At the age of nine he was arrested for stealing a fifty-nine-cent necklace from a dimestore. Within a month he was arrested again and this time an angry judge sent him to a training school, where his education was completed. In the training school he was assaulted homosexually by a number of boys, but then the leader in his cottage fought to claim Ralph Mills for himself. Ralph Mills became the lover of the leader of his cottage and this gave him protection from the other youthful homosexuals. When he left the training school he became a loner on West 118th Street. He had progressed beyond the gang stage. He occupied himself by picking up men on 42nd Street and entertaining them for fees ranging from one dollar to five dollars. In his fourteenth year he was arrested by a patrolman, but then the patrolman forced him to submit to what is called an unnatural act. From this point on, he not only sold himself to homosexuals but he took a delight in beating them, often nearly castrating the men he sucked by biting on their penis until he almost bit through the muscle. He was almost murdered one night in a parking lot off Eighth Avenue and Times Square when a customer forced his teeth apart and then set about beating Ralph Mills.

"On the afternoon of the murder he was walking with his friend Walter Simmons, who participated in the murder, toward a cafeteria on Broadway in the Nineties that is frequented by homosexuals and drug addicts. I went to the home of Walter Simmons. He lives in the same building as Ralph Mills. His mother was legally married, but his father also took the black man's divorce and deserted Mrs. Simmons when she gave birth to her second child. Walter Simmons is fifteen years old. His mother is forty-three years old. Not once has Mr. Simmons attempted to contact his wife or his children. He has vanished. It was simple for Mr. Simmons to vanish. He had no trade, no roots, no skills, no job that would keep him identified with a Social Security number; no one really wanted him except the Department of Welfare, so that they could try and fulfill their fictional responsibility of trying to secure support from Mr. Simmons for his family. Mrs. Simmons has been receiving public welfare for the past eleven years. She is an attractive woman, as most Negro women are attractive, with a sense of unfulfilled promise about them. She told me that Walter was always a good student. She said his reading level was higher than his grade level, that he visited the library, that he received good marks in all of his subjects. She said there was talk at the school of Walter getting a scholarship to an Eastern university because they were always looking for Negro boys with excellent school records. I think you know that less than one percent of the children who have grown up on public welfare ever get to college. Surely ninety-nine percent of them are not unfit for college.

"Because she was legally married, Mrs. Simmons was entitled to a four-room apartment in a public housing site. She was living in the site when Mr. Simmons deserted her. When Walter Simmons was eleven years old the family were evicted from their apartment. A boy friend of Edith Simmons, the oldest daughter of Mrs. Simmons, was arrested on the grounds of the housing site for the possession of narcotics. Edith Simmons was with him at the time of his arrest. Though she wasn't arrested or implicated in the narcotics and was never brought to charges, the director of the public housing site brought eviction proceedings against Mrs. Simmons on the ground that she was an undesirable tenant. She was given immediate notice to move, and instead of fighting this unlawful action—she didn't know how to fight the eviction action, for she had seen it happen to other tenants— she moved.

"The only apartment she could find was in the building on West 118th Street. Mrs. Simmons had to take a back apartment, with a fire escape leading to her bedroom window. She didn't think of buying an iron gate to block off the window. Within a week her television set, her electric iron, her pots and pans, the winter clothes for Walter and her own winter coat were stolen. Edith stayed in the apartment two weeks and then left her mother to live with an addict who quickly introduced her to drugs. Within six months Walter began having asthma attacks. Mrs. Simmons attributed the attacks to the cold rear bedroom. She tried to move, but every apartment that she looked at was worse. Within eight months Walter was failing his subjects at school because he was out most of the time with asthma attacks.

"Walter Simmons and Ralph Mills became close friends. There was no homosexuality between them. Ralph Mills in fact is not a homosexual. He gave himself to men for money and protection. As Mrs. Simmons told me, Walter and Ralph saw in each other what neither of them had. They took to staying out late, mostly supported on the money Ralph Mills earned by permitting himself to be violated by the homosexuals in the Times Square area of New York.

"On the day of the murder Walter Simmons had an asthma attack. He didn't go to school. School for him had ceased to exist once they left the housing project. He had stopped reading, stopped going to the library. He was truly like a man or a boy who is thrown into an unlit cell with no knowledge of why he has been thrown into the cell, with no jailors to come for him, no visitors, no news from the outside world, nothing but his isolation.

"On the morning of the double murder of Mr. and Mrs. Reid, the two boys, Ralph Mills and Walter Simmons, were in isolation from the normal life of children. By all the rules they should have both been sitting in a classroom. Ralph Mills had $5.75 in his pocket. He invited Walter Simmons to see a movie on 42nd Street. They went to 42nd Street and saw a double feature, getting out of the movie about 1:15. Ralph treated Walter to three pieces of pizza pie and they then took a bus up to Central Park West and 85th Street. Walter had heard that his father was hanging around the blocks on Central Park West and they often walked the Central Park West blocks in the Eighties and Nineties, looking into the faces of the men sprawled out on the benches, thinking they could spot Walter's father from the photograph that still hung in the living room. They would also go into the apartment buildings where the doors were never locked, looking for whatever they could steal. On 91st Street they picked up an iron bar. The iron bar was about fifteen inches long and about an inch and a half thick. When they approached the building where S. T. West lived and where the aged couple was murdered, they saw the doorman going out for a cigarette break. They looked into the lobby and saw nothing to steal. They pressed the elevator button; the door opened and they entered the elevator. They still carried the iron bar they had found on West 91st Street. A young girl entered the elevator, but they didn't bother her. They rode the elevator to the top floor, which is where West lived, and they rode to the fifth floor and then up to the tenth floor, and then the aged couple pressed the elevator button on the fifth floor. When the aged couple entered the elevator, Ralph Mills asked Mr. Reid if he had a cigarette. Mr. Reid instinctively reached for his cigarettes and then stopped as he noticed the youth of the two boys. It was then too late.

Ralph smashed him over the head with the iron bar, and before Mrs. Reid could scream, her head was smashed. Ralph repeatedly smashed their skulls, obliterating any trace of the faces of the two people on the floor of the elevator. They then robbed the dead bodies, taking Mr. Reid's wallet, his wrist watch, a diamond ring from the finger of Mrs. Reid. They left the murder car on the third floor, going down the steps, out of the building before the doorman returned. They didn't discuss the murder as they walked toward Broadway. They had merely killed two people who disturbed them as most of us kill a buzzing fly that disturbs us on a summer day without any thought as to the destiny of the fly. There was no time to plan the murder, but the murder had been embedded in them and it took only a moment for the murder to be done. That is why we are all here today. What more could West have found out if he had lived and spoken to Mrs. Mills and Mrs. Simmons, to the neighbors, to the people on the block, to the boys, what more could he have learned or what could he have done?"

Emerson looked toward the casket that enclosed West and said, "He could have defended them. But do they need defense? In his aristocratic way—for West was an aristocrat, if only an American aristocrat—he might have risen in the courthouse on Foley Square and in his eloquent manner, in his sense of justice acquired as much from life as from books, he could have spoken out for Ralph Mills and Walter Simmons, using, like a Catholic priest, a language the boys couldn't understand. Because of this he probably knew that any kind of defense was useless and his heart coiled into a knot. Toward the end of his life West was looking for a murder, a murder that could satisfy his sense of justice. He thought I might or would become such a murderer."

Even the minister, John Holmes Marsh, hunched forward.

"West was part of the movement that I call the new abolitionists. These are people disturbed by the life forced on black persons in the United States. The new abolitionists are powerless to do anything except in a limited way, just as the older abolitionists were limited to rescuing individual slaves, helping to man the underground railways, sheltering escaping Negroes, finding them employment, and they tried to forget in their own minds, both the old abolitionists and the new abolitionists, that the North has more restrictions on the real freedom of the Negro than the South. Today we have men marching in demonstrations, protesting, making pilgrimages to the South, delivering statements to Washington, contributing to the support of Negro students, opening the gates of Harvard and Yale, defending Negroes in court, and, if possible, each tries to become a friend of a Negro. But this they find is impossible.

"And this extraordinary question, why it is impossible to be a friend of a Negro, this question tortured S. T. West and he never had an answer for it. For West was as free as a man can be in America. He had his own law practice. He had an independent income. He made his own friends. They weren't forced on him by his job or neighborhood. He had a wide circle of friends who kept

22

him well informed.

"He and I could have been friends. Why not? I left divinity school because I could not find God, and West entered his church because he had to have a God. But West never viewed me as a friend. He viewed me as a possible murderer. For he thought that I hated white people to such an extent that I would one day have to satisfy my anger by killing a white person. But West was enough of a religious man to know or to reason that I would not kill just any white man, or kill in anger, but only kill in a situation that would unfold, at least for him, the reasons why with his unbounded freedom he could not make friends with a Negro. Not just himself, but all of America. But now he is dead and he will never know the answer."

Emerson stepped away from the pulpit and I thought the crowded hot chapel was going to rise up like a Gothic column and cry out, "Tell us, we want to know!" But there was only silence, a silence as dead as the body of West. I had tears running down my face. I couldn't stop crying and I didn't want to stop crying. I hadn't cried since the war, when I saw bodies heaped up in piles awaiting a common grave because there was no way even in death of identifying the men.

The minister, John Holmes Marsh, came forward and began the psalm that awaits us all. The words came hard out of him, as though he were inventing them for the first time. Words are important, language is important, books are important: this is what Emerson had told me five nights ago. Language is the way we know one another. A poet three thousand years ago wrote the words now being said on Madison Avenue at the death of S. T. West. What words of Emerson's would be remembered ten minutes after West's body left the chapel? As the body of West proceeded up the aisle the minister said, " 'The Lord is my shepherd, I shall not want. He maketh me to lie down in green pastures: he leadeth me beside the still waters. He restoreth my soul: he leadeth me in the paths of righteousness for his name's sake. Yea, though I walk through the valley of the shadow of death, I will fear no evil: for thou art with me; thy rod and thy staff, they comfort me. Thou preparest a table before me in the presence of mine enemies: thou anointest my head with oil; my cup runneth over. Surely goodness and mercy shall follow me all the days of my life: and I will dwell in the house of the Lord forever.' "

The aisle immediately filled with pushing bodies anxious to get back to their desks, where there was order and routine. I had my own desk at the Eaton Foundation to go back to. All of us in the chapel had desks and titles. I was the director of the Eaton Foundation. Charles Eaton, who was the president of the Foundation, gave me a free hand to carry out urban studies that no one else would undertake, to investigate horrors like the West Side of New York City, to find out what the Washington officials were really doing with hundreds of millions of dollars and the American conscience, the new world of Washington officials whose new job it was to save America from itself. The most important of them I saw coming up the aisle, and he gave me a weak smile, the Under

Secretary I used to see on Constitution Avenue who would show me his confidential charts on the black population, charts that he kept in plastic folders, that he handled as though they were the most secret documents in all of Washington. Emerson's eulogy must have made him sick to his stomach. When S. T. West first told me about Emerson he told me that Emerson had attended Exeter, Harvard and the Yale Divinity School. West said none of these schools had made Emerson forget his past or his future, which was to be a stranger in a strange land. Emerson made me feel that I was more of a stranger in my own land than I had ever suspected.

I didn't really know these people pushing into the aisle, checking their watches to see if the service had run longer than they expected. I hadn't known them until S. T. West brought me to meet Emerson. And after meeting Emerson, I found myself ignoring the reports on my desk with titles like "Summaries of Training Projects Funded Under P.L. 87-274," studies that ran into thousands of pages without a single word of humanity. S. T. West told me that Emerson had spent the past twenty-seven years of his life searching for a victim. Perhaps the victim that all of us in the emptying chapel were supposed to be looking for from our desks. I gave up most of my activities at the Foundation to follow Emerson in his search. I became haunted by what haunted S. T. West, for he saw in Emerson a divinity student who was really a murderer, a murderer who, once he found his victim, would commit a murder that would reveal to America its crime against blackness.

On Madison Avenue in the afternoon sun, misty as New York can be, the spire of the Chrysler Building a distant point in the sky, the traffic rumbling past the black car waiting to take West to wherever we go when we are done with this world and time, I saw Emerson standing alone, looking, as I was looking, at the movement of people who were still extraordinarily alive. I walked over to Emerson. He smiled as I neared him. "C'mon," he said, "let's walk north up Madison Avenue into where it becomes Harlem and the first little black bastard that we come to on the street, let's pat him on his head and tell him that the whole world is waiting for him if only he will grab it up in his arms before he dies or is dead."

We started walking up Madison Avenue, past the Eighties, past the shops squeezed together in unbroken lines, the windows filled with bits and daubs of twenty centuries: an Egyptian stone head, a shattered Greek face, Roman coins, Mexican beads, Irish glasses, English plates, Chinese lacquer, French ormolu. Emerson paid no attention to the shops, nor the buildings soaring above the shops, nor the people on the sidewalk who were as far away in time for him as the Roman coins. At 96th Street we came to the boundary. I almost expected to see a border guard stationed on the south side of 96th Street and Madison Avenue. Beyond 96th Street lay the world of Harlem, part of that separate empire America has colonized for three hundred years.

We crossed with the green light. No guard stopped us. It isn't necessary to station physical guards at the 96th

Street boundary. They have long ago been stationed in our minds: thousands and thousands of guards, ready to spring into action each time a white man and a black man look at each other, each guard immediately knowing what gesture, word, thought, he has to protect, as though each thought and word were life itself. It is a battle fought by two hundred million people daily, into the night and sleep. The guards are never at rest, and every border, every boundary of the mind, is as clearly visible as the Great Wall of China.

WE LEFT Madison Avenue and turned into Harlem, walking past the men on the stoops on West 111th Street who stared at us with hate because it appeared that we had a destination to our walk. West's death showed in Emerson's words, his eyes as we walked toward the church on West 112th Street. I could see Emerson's eyes take in the spectacle of Harlem, the big overwhelming ugly mass of people and buildings that had risen up to kill West and that could kill him.

There is a phrase from an old religion that says God made us forgetful so that we would forget about death, for if a man always thought about his own death he would never be able to marry, have children, work or build a house. A phrase from S. T. West came to me. West had said to me, "We're all like that Roman emperor, all of us, when it comes to color, we all wish the black people in America had one neck so that we could get rid of them with a single blow of a sword."

The rain fell as we got to Emerson's church, a soft rain. Emerson opened the door. Then I saw him again in his church. This was where he felt most at home. The church was empty, but no church is ever empty. Emerson wasn't the minister. It was a storefront church, a church made out of a clothing store. The walls were painted white. A wooden cross hung over the altar, carved by a fifteen-year-old drug addict. The church had no minister. The last minister had fled. Emerson worked with the children who still came to the church, children who didn't know the name of the Mayor of the city of New York, the President of the United States, who couldn't count ten numbers in a row or read two pages of the English language, but who could murder.

In the old religions men used to leave their congregations, their comfortable homes, their wives, their children, and go off like beggars into the world to learn what they had forgotten, going as strangers among the people, getting involved in lives they had never known, listening to new voices in the markets, in schools, listening to children, the aged, the sick, the mothers, the dying. These ancient religious men wandered without money, without protection, across deserts and mountains, dependent for their survival on the people they met in their wandering. This kind of wandering refreshed their lives. They learned to listen again to the voices of people. They learned not to be frightened of the deep wells in their ears and minds, not to be frightened of change, youth, themselves. This is the way Emerson came to his church.

In the old religous writing too there is an idea of life that Emerson told me about, an idea which says that when a man is unknown even to himself, when no one can grasp him, when everything eludes him except the certainty of his own existence, then he is nothing. This is

the condition of a man before his real creation, the creation of himself and what he does with his days on earth.
The time of this nothing is chaos. We all experience
chaos. We all hope to come out of the chaos, out of
nothingness, to be created, to have an identity that only
we can possess, that others can recognize, that we know
is ours. In the state of nothingness men live suspended
lives, men are like seeds with the earth overpowering
them.

Negro men are forced to live this way all of the time,
Emerson had said to me that day; no root is permitted to
form, no growth to take place, or God to intervene.

What happened between Emerson and West I call
the Emerson File. I was the observer. And in the end I
became their witness.

THE EMERSON FILE

MEMO ON A PHONE CALL from S. T. West I got five months ago, West saying: "I'm going to give a cocktail party on the twentieth. I'd like you to take a closer look at Emerson. You remember him from the lunch at the Rue Jacques. There'll be about fifty people at the party, but I think the only other person who will interest you will be Jenny Beal. She's a Southern white girl Emerson has slept with. I think the white Southern women can crack open the South if we can get them out of their matrimonial whorehouses. See you on the twentieth."

The Rue Jacques is a French restaurant on East 55th Street. Emerson read the menu printed in French as easily as he read the faces that stared at him. It was at this first lunch that I got the feeling S. T. West had an interest in Emerson way beyond discussing his work in the storefront church on West 112th Street. S. T. West talked constantly about murder during the lunch, nervously, and he seemed to be annoyed that neither Emerson nor I expressed ourselves on the subject of murder. I had a vague, intuitive, threatening feeling, even then, that S. T. West saw in Emerson a murderer. It was fashionable for intellectual white men to see in every black man a murderer and for intellectual black men to see themselves as murderers. But S. T. West was no fool about murder. He had conducted over seventy-five murder trials. He knew murderers. He knew why men killed. He said it was always to remove the odds against themselves. But what kind of odds could a black man remove by committing murder if the odds were 20,000,000 against 180,000,000? S. T. West became more direct. He said to Emerson, "In the Watts riots there were thirty-four or thirty-seven people murdered. In the New York riots there were two or three people murdered. I kept wondering why only thirty-four people were murdered in Watts and not thirty-four hundred or thirty-four thousand. Would you have killed if you had been in the Watts riots?" Emerson smiled, the black-man smile, the secret smile of the black man when he hears a white man say something stupid, but it's rare for the black man to put the white man right.

It seemed that neither I nor Emerson spoke during the lunch. S. T. West dominated the conversation. I remember West saying, "A Watts riot is like a war. A riot brings everyone together in a glorious moment where everyone has a common purpose, which is exactly what war does. War gives everyone exactly what they want out of life: a common goal and an enemy they can name. Maybe the war against the blacks in America is this kind of war, a continual, unending war that gives everyone a personal sense of satisfaction. If this is so, then we'll never see an end to it. Just as the South can't bring the

Civil War to an end. It was the only time those Southern bastards saw a purpose to their existence."

S. T. West suggested we try the strawberries in wine. Emerson ordered apple pie, which I thought was a perfect comment on the lunch.

Two DAYS before the cocktail party, S. T. West, with his timing as a trial lawyer, sent me the following note:

"I'm enclosing this extraordinary 'application' letter from Emerson that I mentioned over the phone. I asked Emerson to send me a résumé so that I could send a letter of recommendation to the church board to set him up as director of the storefront church on West 112th Street. This is the kind of work a 'prominent Protestant layman' does, as you know. The Emerson application speaks for itself. I got Emerson the job, but this letter never got to the church board. As is obvious, it would never have got him the job. And he didn't write it for a church board. Emerson obviously wants the one thing that will ruin him—freedom. Then he'll find he's even more out and alone. Emerson strikes me as the one black man, the only one I have ever met, who will one day make me understand blackness."

Emerson's résumé went into the file. From my windows of the Eaton Foundation on the thirty-fifth floor I can see tens of thousands of windows on Madison Avenue, Fifth Avenue, Sixth Avenue, Broadway, windows stretching down to the foggy tip of Manhattan Island. In every office behind every window each man has a résumé. An industry has grown up around the writing of résumés because most men are afraid to write their own. In a résumé a man has to show why he should be selected for a new station in life. The résumé is submitted at the time of application for a new job. The résumé must be neither too bold nor too diffident. In one-line sentences a man has to state what he has done with his life from the time he left high school or college. A résumé seldom begins before this point in life. But industry and the Federal government have gone further back in time. They know that a man's life begins the day of his birth. They know a man learns just about everything he will ever learn by the time he is eight years old. They know that twenty percent of adult intelligence is developed by the age of one, fifty percent by the age of four and eighty percent by the age of eight. Beyond the age of eight, most men only learn that there is a world they must conform to. The industrial psychologists and the government headhunters have worked up tests that go beyond the résumé, tests that peel away the one-sentence entries, tests to test if a man has really learned this lesson. Their job is to make certain that a man will conform. To conform is everything as the world gets smaller and smaller and more dangerous—even in a storefront church.

Thomas Emerson sent this résumé to S. T. West to secure the job as director of the Protestant storefront church on West 112th Street:

I attended that rich preparatory school Exeter. Black boys are accepted for scholarships if they come to the attention of the Protestant recruiters. How did I come to the attention of the recruiters? The prep schools were conducting a headhunting campaign for black boys. They sent envoys into the black world, trying to track down black students who could read and write. I was one of them.

My mother wanted me to go. My father didn't want me to go. He said, Those white bastards will tear you apart, you'll be a freak. He was right. I was a freak at Exeter. But at least I was a freak who learned what Caesar wrote, and Horace, and Juvenal, and Melville. I even had one teacher who was dying to put his hands on me. I knew his kind by sight from the age of four. From Exeter I went to Harvard. What did I learn at Harvard? Harvard isn't a university. It's a place where you learn your station in life. There are some black boys at Harvard too. We used to stare at one another as we crossed Harvard Square, like whores in a small town who can recognize one another. I spent my free time at Harvard in bed with white girls from Radcliffe who enjoyed this kind of extension course in American history. They used to look at my cock as if it had two heads. I think they all expected me to have six balls.

From Harvard I went to Yale Divinity School, where God is on the board of directors. I left Yale Divinity School because after two years I couldn't get an appointment with God. It seemed insane to be a divinity student unless you heard a call, a rustling in the wind, a cry of unhappy birds, a blinding sun spot in front of your eyes that you knew was God. A sweet tenderness such as you feel when you know you are talking to a person who listens. This didn't happen at Yale. God was always at board meetings. I didn't see or feel God. The divinity students didn't seem to care if God was available. They were better off without God. But I needed God at Yale. I needed to know that all of the words in The Book were real, could be real. That God was as real as my mother wanted him to be. You know that every black woman lives by the Bible. The Bible has been their book. The Bible has given the black women a hold on the world the black man has never had. The black women believe the words of Job, Isaiah, God when he speaks. They know from the Bible how big the world is. They haven't been squeezed into one dirty little tight corner of the world like the black man. They don't grow up like the black men with a tombstone already over their heads, spending the rest of their days trying to push it up. This is what my mother gave me when I left for Exeter, Harvard and Yale: The Book.

I left Yale in the middle of my second year. I got on a bus and came to New York, which is more representative of our present God than Yale. I went directly to West 88th Street, up three flights of crumbling dirty stairs, to the room of a friend from Harvard. He had a doctorate in English literature and nothing else because he suffered from the black sickness, blackness. He had a miserable little room, but there was a cot where I could sleep.

On the first night he gave a party for me. He invited a

book editor, a teacher and two white girls who talked for ten minutes about the plastic coils they were wearing at the threshold of their cervixes. There was a person I can only describe as an idiot. He had achieved minor fame by writing an article saying that if he had a daughter he would not let his daughter fuck a black man or marry a black man because he couldn't tolerate a black man for a son-in-law. The idiot had achieved this fame because the article appeared in a magazine that always wrote about the black man as though the black man would be all right if he just spent another five hundred years learning what the editors knew. What the idiot didn't write in his article was that while he was writing the article his wife was in bed with my friend, a black man. This bit of gossip was given to me by my doctoral friend.

I woke up early my first morning in New York. About 5 a.m. I was on the cot, half dozing, half awake. I saw my doctoral friend get out of bed, go over to the sink, rinse out a spoon, put some powder in the spoon, heat it, reach in the kitchen drawer for a needle and as though he was taking a morning cup of coffee, he injected heroin into his system. I asked him over coffee why he was on junk. He said why not. I asked him where he got the money. He told me without shame that he had developed an amazing control over his sphincter muscle that earned him $150 a week from three homosexual doctors he visited, and he would stay on junk as long as his muscles held out. He said I could stay in his room until I found a place, but I left that afternoon because I didn't want to be there if the police kicked in his door.

I had $115 in my pocket. I didn't want a room in Harlem then. Harvard had done that to me. I walked the streets between Central Park West and Riverside Drive in the West 90's looking for a room. I went into one foul building that I had never seen equaled in Harlem. I saw dazed old men sitting around filthy hotel lobbies. I rode in elevators that stank. I saw babies crawling on floors covered with human droppings because the toilets were all stuffed up with newspapers. I saw enough junkies to fill Lexington, Kentucky. I saw whores, drunks and the dazed faces of people let out of Rockland State Hospital to survive on pills. I finally rented a room on West 99th Street. I spent a week in that room. There was no color line in the building. Riding the elevator was like a Yale divinity professor's idea of Hell. But I was outside the life of the building. I couldn't remain there for more than a week. The black whores, the white whores, the white faggots, the black faggots, the black addicts, the white addicts, the white psychopaths, the black psychopaths, the sick, the diseased, the babies, they all lived in perfect integration.

I found a room on West 77th Street. I was within a three-minute walk of the Museum of Natural History. I found myself going to the museum, wandering through its fantastic halls, until from day to day I began to feel growing in me a sense of time reaching back to the rain forests, the great glaciers, those animals that still seem to exist in us as tortured forms of life that some of the undergraduates at Harvard saw when they sucked on a cube of sugar soaked with LSD. I stared at those great museum display windows on the first floor with the life-size figures of the early settlers, the early Indians but not the black man. It wasn't necessary to put the black man on display.

My mother started me reading the creation of the world when I was three. By the age of five I could read Genesis by myself, which I still do. The Bible became my family history. It's always hard for white people to understand why black people sound so intelligent even when they're illiterate. The Bible, dear prominent Protestant, the Bible was written to make people intelligent about the world they live in. But the black people made a terrible, terrible mistake. The black people in America read the Bible for comfort, not for instruction. If the Bible had been read for instruction I wouldn't be writing to you today as a representative of a distant and inaccessible race, the W.A.S.P.

You want to know what kind of work I did in New York when I left Yale? I was a messenger. A dishwasher. A reader for a blind professor. I worked as a porter in a nursing home on Central Park West. I delivered groceries in the center of the world of the "beautiful people." The grocery store was located near 73rd Street and Madison Avenue. With the authority of my white delivery jacket and boxes of groceries, I penetrated Fifth Avenue, Madison Avenue, Park Avenue. Twice I lay in king-size beds with white women who had nothing to do that morning or any other morning. I delivered messages to TV producers, movie producers, book editors, magazine editors, foundations. For three weeks I went from one messenger company to another, delivering messages on Wall Street, 42nd Street, the West Side, the East Side, until I saw the inside of the great law firms, the great publishing houses, the great TV offices, the great insurance offices on Williams Street, the great downtown banks with their flags flying like medieval knights. I saw the representatives of the high and mighty world which you, and which most of the students who sat next to me at Harvard, enter at birth. I saw no black people. It is mysterious to me how the black people are hidden in New York. How can a million people be hidden away? This is another miracle, Dear W.A.S.P.

I spent three days with a friend in his home in St. Albans, New York. St. Albans is completely black. For three days I didn't see a white person. This is an uncommon experience, Dear W.A.S.P., to be had within 35 minutes of Times Square. At night I heard the complaints. My friend graduated from Harvard with a master's degree in history. His wife is a probation worker. Together they earn $16,000 a year. Their baby lives ten hours a day with his grandmother. The baby spoke with the grandmother's Georgia accent, here in New York City. The oldest boy went to grade school. The wife said, "He goes to an all-black school. When I lived in Manhattan I never went to an all-black school." For dinner she cooked enough food for ten people. He said, "Jews only speak to Jews; what's so wrong about black people only speaking to black people?" She said, "He only sees black children in that school." "What the hell is so wrong with that!" She said, "If you don't know, then you

don't want to know." He said, "Your boy won't ever be
in some fucking miserable juvenile term court with some
white prick playing the law guardian." She said, "He'll be
a vegetable, he'll be a bright, clean, educated vegetable."
He said, "You bitch, do you think anybody is bigger than
history! Do you think any black man in this fucking
country can ever be anything but a black man until the
majority of people in this country decide otherwise? And
they'll decide it without laws, without legislation, without stupid fantastic presidential proclamations; and until
they decide it, in whatever way they choose, what you
think, my dear, what anybody thinks, doesn't mean a
goddamn thing." She said, "Is that what they taught you
at Harvard?" He said, "Baby, Harvard taught me how to
make a living. Without the nine grand I get for teaching
American history to a bunch of idiots you'd be living in
some fucking middle-income project in the middle of
Harlem where they wash the walls down with a mixture
of piss and iodine."

They went at it this way for two hours. I didn't say
much. They didn't ask me. They didn't have anyone else
they dared to argue in front of. I seemed to be the first
person in a long time to set them off. Before we went to
sleep the wife brought out brandy, coffee, cheese, Scotch,
demitasses. Later I heard them in bed. Nothing could
shut out the sounds. Did he wear a condom, did she swallow pills, use a coil? Were they making another baby, a
black baby? In the morning the wife prepared pancakes,
waffles, bacon, eggs, herring, coffee. They had *The New
York Times* and the *Daily News* delivered. My friend

looked worried, as though he wanted his wife to spend the morning douching. He gave me a couple of dumb smiles. "Do you want to go to church?" he asked me. "Is it a black church or a white church?" I asked him. "A white church," he said. "Which is another thing," the wife said, "the three hundred dollars a year we give to that church is making me sick. I'd rather spend that money on Classic Comic books. Why doesn't that minister dare open his mouth, why doesn't he try to squeeze a word out? If he's frightened, then it means we're frightened too." He said, "Baby, you make pretty good pancakes and you make a lousy fucking revolutionist. The smart revolutionist knows when he stands a chance of winning. Not here, Baby. This is black suburbia. Nobody wins here. If you don't like it here, Baby, there are ten thousand families in Harlem waiting to buy this property. The only people fighting in civil rights today, if that's what you're trying to talk about to a couple of ex-Harvard men, are a bunch of idiots who have nothing to lose, a bunch of students, unemployed whites, ministers who can't be fired, old ladies who have run out of charities, some of the white liberals of the 1940's and 1950's who never made it and so they hang on to the only thing that still gives them superiority, a black prick. No, Baby, the boundaries of the world have never been so clearly drawn. Nobody needs a map. With a station wagon you can load up at the supermarket. That's it, Baby, the station wagon and the supermarket, that's what we've got. And between you and me, Baby, that's just about what the white pricks have got too." "The hell with your Har-

vard logic, and stop calling me Baby! Why don't you tell
your friend from Harvard what this really is. This isn't
black suburbia. This isn't the black middle class. We
aren't the black middle class with our $16,000 a year.
There is no black middle class. There's just a black middle without a head or feet to stand on. We're invisible.
Nobody even knows there is a black middle class, do
they, Mr. Harvard? I only know it because I typed your
thesis on it." "Baby," he said, "if you think Mama on
West 137th Street is the answer, with six junkies on the
sidewalk for every one school kid, you know what to do.
Until somebody comes to try and hang me for being
black from the tree out there on the lawn that I bought
for $8.95, I'm going to pretend that I'm as free now as
I'll ever be."

The government form SF 57 that the guys filled out at
Harvard for Federal jobs fascinated me. List every address where you ever lived! I lived for one week in the
Fort Greene low-income housing project. Do you know
what it is to live a lifetime in the Fort Greene housing
project? The project is just across the Brooklyn Bridge. It
is five minutes away from that historic piece of real estate
preserved for Wall Street clerks, Brooklyn Heights. No
such preservation goes on at Fort Greene. My mother's
sister asked me to do her a favor. She had to go into the
hospital for a week to treat a kidney infection. She didn't
want the kids to go to a shelter or a Children's Center or
to split up more than they are now. Her husband walked
out on her after the third child. My mother's sister—I
hate the way "aunt" is pronounced—has five children,

from three years to eleven years old. After the last baby she had her tube cut. Her husband has never called, never written (he can write), never asked about his children. This is the way the black father tries to kill his children when he knows that he can no longer be a father to them.

I spent seven days at the Fort Greene project. Most of the people living in the Fort Greene project are black, which is another way of saying they're all black. I saw addicts, whores, girls of ten and twelve hustling, boys of ten and twelve hustling, heroin sold as openly as Mr. Softee ice cream. On a bench while I was taking care of my sister's two youngest asthmatic children a uniformed housing policeman told me there was nothing on this earth in the form of drugs, booze, sex, that I couldn't buy at the low-cost government-sponsored Fort Greene housing project. He proudly told me that he could get me girls age ten, twelve and up, combinations of girls, who would do anything for a price ranging from $1 to $100. The uniformed housing policeman should have been fed into an HEW computer. I learned at Harvard that the Department of Health, Education and Welfare was spending about $10 million a year on research projects to determine why the housing projects are a nightmare. I could have told them the answer for fifty cents. The housing projects were built to house a nightmare. Who lives at the Fort Greene project? Women abandoned by their husbands, children abandoned by their fathers, mothers and children abandoned by everyone except the check that arrives every two weeks from that institution that has replaced the white Southern slave plantation owner, the Department of Public Disposal.

I had three weeks on 9th Street in the Village. At a Harvard party I met a white girl from Smith College. I was told she had been thrown out of the Peace Corps after being caught in the tent of a local black chieftain in Ethiopia. She landed in New York and decided not to go back to Akron, Ohio. The Peace Corps let her resign because it wouldn't be good on her future SF 57's to say she had been thrown out of the Peace Corps for scoring a black chief. Most of the people I knew at Harvard wouldn't sign up for the Peace Corps. They had heard about the Peace Corps psychologicals. This girl was teaching at a West Side private school where the black middle class in Manhattan send their black babies. The black middle class hates the public schools, she said to me at the Harvard party when she thought she was drunk. She rented three rooms for $235 a month. Nobody in her elevator knew who I was when I moved in, and nobody dared to ask. Some of the whites trembled when they rode up in the elevator with me, and I didn't blame them. Her building had had fifty robberies in two months. Somebody has to support the junkie population in the Village. I mention this in my application, Dear W.A.S.P., because if I am going to work in a church of God, I have to show some of the ways of God.

What are to be my duties in the house of God? To love God? Teach God to young black children? Interpret God? Follow God blindly? Do business with God? Argue with God? Pray to God to take time off for the souls of little black children? Enlist God? Curse God for having flown over West 112th Street without blessing the black children? Take God by the hand and lead him into the black streets, to the black faces, the black hearts of the black people who never learned how to pray or deal with God? What am I to do with the black children of whom you so neatly said, "They need a church"? What kind of church? Do you want me to play jazz records for them? Read modern poetry? Buy them oils and watercolors and brushes and have them smear paint in a pretense of art? Art isn't for children. Art is for grown men. Religion isn't for children. Instruction is for children. This is the great, great difference between the Jewish children and the other children. The Jewish people have instructed their children while the Christians have always taught religion to their children. This is the mistake the blacks made when they learned to read their Bibles in the South.

What are to be my duties in the new church you are preparing? I ask you and the other Protestants who are just beginning to discover America. I heard the arguments for storefront churches three years ago at Yale. "Why don't we have storefront churches in the Negro neighborhoods, why don't we bring religion to them, why don't we create a real church out of the most real ideas that we have in Protestant theology?" a divinity professor at Yale said in a seminar. "Why don't we take over empty stores and make them into churches? What is a church but a minister and the people who listen to Him and the minister? I am willing to say that storefront churches can probably do more good than all of the projects, demonstrations, community action programs, welfare programs, delinquency programs, studies, research— in a word, all of the nonsense that we've been burying our minds in to obscure from ourselves the truth that when we talk about urban decay what we really mean to talk about is the calculated decay of the Negro soul." I said to him, "Harlem, you know, is covered with churches. Harlem has more churches than any other neighborhood in New York. New York City now has 1,724 Protestant churches. Do you think another 17,000 churches would make a difference to the decayed black soul?" This is the kind of question a young black divinity student asks a white professor who he thinks has never walked down the block between Seventh Avenue and Eighth Avenue on West 145th Street.

What are my qualifications for the job you propose? I can type. I can run a mimeographing machine. I can play the piano. I can recite the first six chapters of Genesis. I know the prophets better than I know most of my relatives in Baltimore. I can drive an automobile. I can operate a tape recorder. I can write a sermon. I can play baseball, basketball, tennis, swim and water-ski. I have a B.A. from Harvard and what I call an association with Yale. I've never had syphilis or a mental breakdown. I have never injected heroin into my arm. I find marijuana a bore. I have no out-of-wedlock children, to use the technical phrase. I have never been married. My father is still alive. My mother is still alive. I have two brothers and one sister. One brother is a post-office clerk in Baltimore, the youngest brother teaches high school in a black school in Atlanta. My sister is married and she lives in Cleveland, Ohio, practicing birth control. She is afraid to give birth to a black baby. I have never been arrested. I weigh 165 pounds, I am 5 feet 11 inches tall. My father will retire from the post office in 1968. My mother spends most of her time now in the living room seated at a big round oak table that I remember my father buying at a Salvation Army furniture store for $12. She reads and reads the Bible until it has lost all meaning except an unassailable comfort.

What was my last place of employment?

A New York State training school for boys from age eight to age thirteen. The courts still send boys of eight to jail. A training school is a jail, a prison. Any child deprived of his liberty is in a prison. I was hired as a teacher. But none of the boys in the training school could read! How fantastic! Why couldn't they read? But why should they read? What meaning could words have for them? Nobody wanted them to read.

They can learn to read. I proved it by teaching a nine-year-old boy from my old block on West 126th Street to read in three weeks.

I stayed at the training school nine weeks. The training school had a budget of $1 million for 250 boys. For five years the New York state legislature turned down a budget request from the school for five remedial teachers, even though 97 percent of the boys at the school can't read. More than eight out of ten of the boys committed acts that brought them back to the training school after their discharge: this gossip was told to me on

my first day at the school. The school was in the open
green country of upstate New York. But the clear air was
offensive, the sky offensive, the green hills offensive.
Moses knew what he was doing when he took the Jews
into the wilderness. From then on the Jewish people were
prepared for any kind of wilderness that could be thrown
at them. The only mistake the Jewish people ever made
was in Germany, where they believed in the law only to
find at the gates of Treblinka that there was no law. Here
in America the black people have never been in a wilderness. They have always lived on the bounty of the whites,
never in a wilderness. The training school was soft. It
sucked the children into coming back. Everything about
the training school was designed to make the black children soft, superfluous, dependent. The technical achievement of America in destroying the black man is one of
the great psychological marvels of the world. I left the
training school the way I left Yale, to get away from failure.

I came back to New York and started sleeping with a
white teacher I knew who had gone to Vassar. She
taught in a Harlem school. And for a pleasant change,
she didn't want my black cock drained. She was a great
teacher with the black fifth-grade children from 9 a.m. to
3 p.m. She told me that she had thirty-four children in
her class. She said twenty-eight of them didn't have the
faintest notion of what was going on in the classroom.
Most of them were psychopathetic, a word that I have
invented to describe these black children. She said she
concentrated most of her attention on the six children

who she thought could learn something. It was wrong, but she didn't know what else to do. I liked her. She was a crazy white girl. She liked to walk through Harlem. She thought teaching in the black school gave her an umbrella, a coating of black, a protection. It didn't. She would go through Harlem alone. Walk the streets, which she said was more of a demonstration than marching in Alabama or Washington. A gang of black boys grabbed her one night. They got her up to a roof. They fucked her until they got tired. Then they threw her off the roof. She hit the sidewalk on West 128th Street head first. The six black kids in her class who she thought might make it became as crazy as the other twenty-eight. I went to her funeral. The whole damn school turned out. There was nobody in the school who could sum up her death so that it could have meaning for all of the crazy white teachers and the crazy black kids in the school.

Dear W.A.S.P., this is the world I have inhabited. Believe me, there is more. You asked me if I need a job. Yes, I need a job. Why do I want to work in a storefront church now on West 112th Street? Because I always prefer to be where God has some opportunity of showing us that he is God. If this is too obtuse, then I prefer to be where I can show God where I stand. Yours, Thomas Emerson.

I WAS LATE getting to West's cocktail party. A fight on the West 72nd Street platform of the IRT subway delayed the train. S. T. West lived on the fifteenth floor of an imposing, ornate, pre-war apartment building in full decay on West 93rd Street. The building had escaped the bulldozers but not decay. The lobby had a faded, worn Oriental rug that had been laid down in 1939. The marble floor was stained and gutted. The old moderne light fixtures still hung from the ceiling, two of the bulbs out. The only new addition was the doorman, who wore a shoulder holster and a thick gold ring with a stamped police shield. He was part of the new world of doormen in New York, retired policemen who haven't turned in their guns. West could easily have moved thirty blocks down to Lincoln Center or a mile across the park into Fifth Avenue, but he preferred to be in the midst of the new terror, as he called it.

Fifteen thousand drug addicts live on the West Side blocks between 72nd Street and 96th Street. Columbia University hires its own police force to patrol the West Side streets off its 116th Street campus while its social-work professors do their research in Lima, Peru. Police dogs patrol buildings in the West 90's. *The New York Times* reports that apartment seekers on the West Side no longer inquire about the rooms, the rent, the terms of the lease; they ask about security systems, police guards, buzzer systems, TV cameras in the lobby, night patrols through the corridors, burglar alarms in each apartment. This is part of the terror of the West Side. The new terror sweeping San Francisco, Los Angeles, Chicago, Cleveland, Detroit, St. Louis.

I traveled to West's apartment on the West Side subway. The subway is part of the new terror. Policemen with guns ride the subway trains, and you feel safe only when you see the policemen with their guns. Everyone on the train sits withdrawn into his terror. You no longer know who will start screaming, pull a knife, threaten to murder because he has been jostled, his foot stepped on, the foot becoming the extension of the soul. Eyes are averted. No one dares look at another person. A misunderstood glance could mean a fight, possibly death. To look into a man's eyes on the subway may mean you hate him, which is why you have singled him out. People are insulted by each other's own existence.

When I rang West's bell, Emerson answered the door. He smiled when he saw me. His hand was hard, his fingers long, wet from the chilled glass he held.

"West is out on the terrace drinking bourbon," Emerson said. "Did you ever meet Jenny Beal?"

"West's mentioned her, but we've never met."

"She's been asking West if you'd arrived yet. C'mon in the kitchen. I'll make you a drink."

A three-foot poster on the foyer wall announced a lecture delivered by S. T. West in 1964 in Columbus, Ohio, on "The Prophets and the Ministers." Emerson led the way through the stand-up drinkers.

"Who's Jenny Beal?" I asked Emerson.

"She's a rich Southern girl who gets around more than most people. West has a letter from her framed in his bedroom. The letter tells West to come to Birmingham if he wants to see the first real black riot. Jenny wrote to West that she could hear the shotguns being loaded. The police dogs getting extra rations. West didn't believe her. The riots broke out two days after West got the letter, which is why West framed the letter together with a headline from *The New York Times.*"

Emerson picked up a bottle of I. W. Harper. "Bourbon?" he asked. "This seems to be bourbon day."

"Bourbon is fine." I took my first good look at Emerson's face as he poured the bourbon. Emerson didn't look like the young black men at West Side parties who seemed to bend from the waist every time you spoke to them. Nor was his face frozen. He had a glimpse of the past in his face, the whole past history of the world. This is the face of the mythological American heroes, Spencer Tracy, Gary Cooper, Humphrey Bogart, a face with a sense of acting on the All, with an unconditioned, secret, unfathomable sense of human action.

"Ready to go to the terrace?" Emerson asked. He handed me a water glass half full of bourbon. We left the kitchen and passed through a room lined with books. One wall was covered with framed photographs of ministers, professors, writers, testimonials West had collected from Protestant organizations, bronze plaques that always seemed to honor the giver more than the recipient. On the desk lay the book West had written about his work as a layman in a black congregation in Harlem and his days in the law office he had opened in Harlem to defend Harlem kids indicted for murder. West kept the law office on 116th Street going for eleven years. He never charged a fee. He defended thirty-seven kids and gave up the law office when New York State stopped burning murderers in the electric chair. West had a harder time working with the black congregation in Harlem. The ministers shoved him out of the church when he began to confuse a congregation that wasn't ready for his silent and stern Episcopalian God.

We walked out to the terrace. New York City lay still, quiet; suddenly it didn't look suicidal. The skyline of New York is simple proof that men are capable of creating beauty even when beauty is their last consideration. It is this beauty that confuses everyone.

"If you have the right button to press," S. T. West said, "it can all go up in smoke sooner than we expect it to." West looked fazed, not drunk but as though he would like to be drunk. He held a glass of whiskey. "This," West said, "is Jenny Beal. And this, Jenny Beal, is John Brooks. And everyone knows Thomas Emerson."

Jenny Beal's face was softer than the faces of the Northern women at the party. The Southern face is soft, swaddled in time because the Southern women are the only women in America who are publicly revered. I liked

57

Jenny Beal. She looked responsible to me. I suppose she bothered the hell out of her Southern father, whoever he was, and her mother. I had known one Southern girl who gave herself up to cleansing the South. She lived in Charleston. She would date Negro men in Charleston. She came to New York. She married a Negro. She became pregnant. Her husband died of a heart attack while she was giving birth at Roosevelt Hospital. She came out of the hospital with no money and a baby. Her husband's heart attack was suicide. He had run out of money and didn't have the strength to start getting fresh money. I saw her in a furnished room in the West 90's. Her mother came from Charleston to bring her home with the baby. The mother wanted to see if the baby's face was black, if it gave off blackness, because if it did, she could not bring the baby back to Charleston. She told me that her husband would have to give up his job and they would have to flee from everyone they knew or had ever known. She said her neighbors knew she had come to New York to bring back the baby and they would study the baby's face to see if it had black blood in it. Her neighbors told her that an Indian baby, a Cuban baby, a Chinese baby, a Spanish baby, a Mexican baby, any baby could be accepted except a black baby. I will never forget seeing her holding her daughter's baby, talking to the baby, asking out loud what the madness was all about, why blackness horrified her neighbors and had horrified her all of her life. Certainly the black women who had held the Southern white babies for generations had asked the same questions about their own black babies.

S. T. West said to Jenny Beal, "Emerson here and Brooks are the only two people I know who think more than what they say out loud. I have yet to hear what either of them thinks."

West held his glass of whiskey poised fifteen stories above West 93rd. Street. He turned his hand and the bourbon splashed out.

"This is what we need," West said, "one good rainfall of bourbon and one good preacher. New York City is ready for a preacher. The most remarkable thing about this remarkable city is the ministers who can run jazz concerts, produce plays of the absurd, sponsor pop art, collect drug addicts, deliver illegitimate babies, write for *The Village Voice*, march in demonstrations, get beaten up in the South, parade all day around hamburger joints and, if necessary, out-bureaucratize the Washington bureaucrats. Think of what a real preacher could do if he took on this city from Spuyten Duyvil to the Battery, this city and this civilization we have here. Think of what all of us here have seen with our own eyes in the last twenty-five years. And then think of a preacher who can make us believe what we have seen and what we have done to one another."

"Why don't you become the preacher?" Emerson said quietly, almost whispering the words.

"Emerson, I'm Episcopalian. I can't go any further than just pronouncing on the unfortunates of the world. I can't get rid of the habit. The only good thing about the Episcopalians is their financing. They don't expect too much help from God. Episcopalians are the most perfect representatives of an impractical and ineffective and inefficient God. This makes us useless as preachers or prophets. A real preacher is a trumpet sounding in the world! I'll know what to do with my preacher when I find him. Every preacher needs a guide. I'll tear down St. John the Divine and rebuild it for him!

"But you can tell us, Emerson, why there isn't a single real church in New York and Harlem, our Harlem that has more people living in it who believe in God than Rome ever had."

"Why?" Jenny asked Emerson, as though they had never spoken to each other before.

Emerson smiled.

"No goddamn smile this time!" West shouted at Emerson. "Why isn't there one single real black church in Harlem!"

The terrace was quiet, so quiet we could hear the rumbling of the voices in the living room, so quiet that we were conscious of the sun passing under the dark water of the Hudson, so quiet that we could see Emerson's face passing through rumblings and intimations denied to us. In this sudden quiet, brought on by West's outburst, Emerson said, more quietly than the silence, "If there weren't a church in Harlem, your throat would have been cut long ago."

"That I believe," West said. "I believe that. I believe it."

S. T. West withdrew into silence, looking like a lawyer who has exhausted himself on a prosecution witness who is telling the truth. Emerson announced he was going into the kitchen to get a bourbon.

Jenny Beal said to me, "Let's go in to the party. By now the guests should be screaming at one another."

They were. When we entered the library a crowd was packed around Charles Woodford, who was black, and George Hackett, who was white. Hackett had written an article for *Harper's Magazine* on the self-hate of the Negro middle class, their refusal to be the salvation of the Negro low-income class. The article had brought Hackett instant fame because nothing makes better reading than something about the refusal of black people to act like white people.

Woodford, a professor of social psychology, was past arguing, he was yelling at Hackett. "You have one million school kids in this fucking city and more than half of them can't read a line of English with comprehension!"

"Whose fault is that?" Hackett yelled back.

"Your fucking fault!" Woodford yelled. "You and the whole goddamn white power educational structure in this stinking city! You made a city, a state, a country where a black boy feels there's no good reason for him to read or write. The books aren't his books! The classrooms aren't his classrooms! It's all white crap!"

Hackett yelled at Woodford, "Why, you ignorant bastard! You can write! You can read! Would you want Polish books in the classrooms? French books? Jewish books? Why don't you find out what the reading level is for Chinese children in this city who attend the public

61

schools in Chinatown? Why don't you find out the reading level of the Italian kids in Little Italy? The black
man loves being a big fat nothing. He loves being taken
off the hook!"

"Your hook!" Woodford shouted.

"Right now there isn't a single intelligent black Negro
leader in this country who dares to tell the truth to the
black people. Isn't that fantastic! Isn't that the hook! If a
white man tries to tell the truth, every fucking black organization in this country is out to murder him!"

"What truth!"

"Read the Labor Department report on the Negro
family. Read what some of the welfare experts are saying.
Read about the discoveries in mental retardation brought
on by a miserable environment! Stop thinking it's the
nineteenth century and equality is for everyone. You
fight for it in the twentieth century. The history books
are in the library. Nobody hides the books. The classrooms are open. Fifty thousand teachers have to report to
work each morning in this city. The city of New York
spends a billion dollars a year for education. *You* get the
black kids to read! *You* get them to learn! You! You!
You!"

Woodford screamed, "Do you think you're telling me
something new! Do you? Do you think you're being bold
with me like some fucking psychoanalyst? Don't you
think I've heard this from every frightened white liberal?
You're frightened, that's why you talk so much. You're
frightened of what you see yourself holding in your hand
after three hundred years of history. Open that bag and

you'll find it's full of shit!"

From the edge of the crowd a white girl standing next to Jenny Beal cried out in a shrill voice, "If you both keep harping on this black-white hate, you and all your kind, you'll really have all of the white families leaving New York City!"

"Get out!" Woodford yelled at her.

It was a signal for the crowd around Woodford and Hackett in the library to break up. Jenny and I went toward the loud excited voices we heard coming from a bedroom. The door was open. More than twenty people were crowded into the room. They were staring at a young Negro who stood against an antique pine highboy. His jacket was off, his shirt sleeve rolled up, exposing a thin naked arm bent into a V.

Jenny pushed forward into the room. She stared at the thin black naked arm, an arm that seemed to be disjointed from its body. The owner of the arm looked twenty-five. His eyes were making an effort to lift themselves beyond the inward vision of an addict.

"Yes," he said, "I'll show you. It's just like taking a blood test. The needle goes into the arm, just here, just like this." He pressed his fingernail into his arm. Jenny gripped my arm.

"Then what happens?" a woman's voice cried out.

"What happens after that the doctors have to explain. Let me tell you something that I have learned. This thing that we call society—in its mysterious way, it doesn't permit a black man to earn enough money to support a black wife and his black children, but it does

63

provide him with the mysterious energy to steal sixty dollars a day."

"Sixty dollars a day for what?" a voice cried out, like a chorus.

"For me. I need sixty dollars a day to live. I can steal sixty dollars a day, day in and day out."

"How?"

"You asked me about heroin. Let me tell you something. The out-of-work, unskilled, isolated, sick, lost black man—most of you know these catchwords—this black man has a nagging thought of wanting to feel alive. This you can believe from me. For this kind of black man, being alive means being alive with heroin. The heroin makes a black man feel alive. Heroin makes a man feel busy. The world goes around for him. He doesn't have to lift a finger except to steal or murder if necessary. That's why you see a foolish smile on the faces of black addicts. The black addict is smiling at the foolishness of his existence. The white addicts all look like sick dogs. They *are* sick dogs. The black addict smiles the way he does because of the way the heroin got into his blood. The crazy things he has to do to get the heroin to stick into his bloodstream. It's funny, but nobody laughs over it. If you're going to get the black man to stop taking heroin, and that's what you people are talking about in here, then you have to give the black addict an existence that isn't foolish and a waste. But maybe you people feel that heroin is a cheap price for keeping the black man foolish."

Anna Burns got up. She lectured at New York University on urban psychology. Anna looked directly at the young addict, facing him like a prosecutor. "If you were the Mayor of the city of New York," she said, "and you had the power to act on the addict problem, what would you do for such a person as you describe?" Anna Burns looked at him as though she had chopped off his head.

"He'll answer the bitch," Jenny whispered to me.

The Negro addict faced Anna Burns. He got up from the edge of the bed. He leaned against the antique pine highboy.

"What would I do with the thirty thousand black addicts—or maybe the sixty thousand black addicts if we count the school kids from eight to fifteen? I don't know what I would do. We don't expect a cancer patient to prescribe his own treatment. You shouldn't expect a person suffering from a social disease to prescribe his own treatment. The Mayor of the city of New York is helpless with the drug addicts. He can't give them life, which is what they need."

"Why not?" a voice cried out. "This city spends over four billion dollars a year!"

"Because this city is perfect for heroin now. This city is as sick as the addicts. You can feel heroin in the air. In the subways. In the cafeterias. In the playgrounds. In the hallways. In the schoolyards. In the rotten air this city breathes. The addict is a dead man. This city is dead now. It doesn't have the strength to care about addicts, just as an addict doesn't have the strength to care about himself. That's why the addicts are multiplying. You don't cure an addict, lady. Life is the only thing that can

65

cure an addict. If an addict sucks dicks for five dollars or steals from cars or robs old ladies and steals from his neighbors in Harlem, if he has fifteen-year-old girls out hustling for him to get money for heroin, he's outside of life. That's why an addict doesn't care about who he hurts, who he steals from or who he kills. He's outside of caring."

Morris Bellows, a psychoanalyst, cried out, "I'm sick of this kind of crap! That's why you stick needles in your arm! A simple question was asked of you. Answer it! How many clinics are needed? What kind of clinic would *you* like to attend? How much heroin do you need on a daily basis? How do you get doctors to work with addicts? How do you get rid of the religious fakers, the social workers who wet in their pants every time they talk about drug addiction? How do you get the addicts to take their place in society, like the diabetics? I'm not equating diabetes with drug addiction, but we don't hound a diabetic for taking insulin. If drug addiction is a social disease, then the simplest thing is to treat it like a disease. Just think of what one hundred thousand diabetics in New York would do to get insulin, if insulin was denied to them."

The addict faced Bellows and said, "You sound like you're saying the right things, but you're saying the wrong things. Maybe these people here don't know the difference. Addicts are not like diabetics or anybody else alive. The addict is trying to maintain existence. He doesn't need a doctor. He doesn't need a clean, efficient government clinic that will stick him full of junk. He doesn't need junk in satisfactory doses. He needs what he'll never get from you because you can't give it to him. He wants existence. Do you know that the cops in those filthy precincts are kinder to addicts than anybody in this whole goddamn city, because the cops in the station houses are the only people who know what addicts go through to steal to get money to buy heroin? It hits the cops right in the middle of their gut. Because the cops know what they have to go through as a cop to get money to keep their families alive. I don't know how I got started on this jerk-off talking."

The addict hurried out, past Anna Burns, past Morris Bellows. His body brushed against Jenny Beal. Jenny Beal seemed to push her body into the addict as he passed, as though the addict were on his way to a religious immolation and she could share in the immolation.

"Let's go get a drink," Jenny said to me.

In the kitchen Emerson sat on a ladder stool, holding a glass of bourbon. He faced the living room that now looked as packed as St. Peter's Square. If Emerson hated white men, I hadn't seen it yet in him. S. T. West wouldn't have spent ten minutes with Emerson if Emerson had a nagging blackness, an infantile blackness, if Emerson accepted the blackness imposed on him and that he only lived to get the white man's goodies. I couldn't see where West had got the idea that Emerson could be a murderer. Unless, in one of those complicated ways that we respond to the All, West felt that Emerson

67

had to murder because West and the entire white race had made it impossible for Emerson ever to live a normal life.

Emerson wore a blue blazer, gray flannels, a white button-down shirt. This was the way he must have looked walking across the grounds of Harvard, of Exeter, of Yale, his face absorbing five thousand years of history without knowing what it meant to him.

"All of these people here make me think of one thing," Emerson said. He turned away from the living room filled with Protestant ministers, Legal Aid lawyers, professors, executive directors of agencies, even an ex-assistant secretary of HEW, the new breed of people who commuted between New York and Washington on the shuttle flights. "Just one thing," Emerson said. "They're murderers."

"How?" Jenny Beal asked. "Who would these people kill?"

"I've been reading the Warren Report on the assassination of President Kennedy. It makes less sense than the McCone Report on Watts," Emerson said. "In Watts the issues were clear. Black men were fighting white men. The black men killed and burned what they thought was white. The Warren Report says nothing to us. It should say that at one point in Lee Oswald's life, when he was about twelve, when he needed a father, a voice, somebody to talk to about his dreams, somebody to talk to about all of the loneliness turning around in his head, there wasn't a single voice in New York City, or even in the entire United States, to speak to him. In the great city of New York, where he was at the time, there wasn't a single person or children's agency or any other kind of agency prepared to listen to him, to talk to him in a way that might have saved Kennedy's life. That's why Kennedy died. Do you remember when the Russians were holding that college professor from Yale and President Kennedy said directly to the Soviet government, Set him free? This was a direct statement from the single most powerful voice in the world at that time, President Kennedy. The mightiest voice on earth opened up to save a single man. There is nothing in the Bible, nothing in human history, like this single act of Kennedy. This happened about a month before Kennedy was killed. It tore into the mind of Lee Oswald. He must have read those headlines in a torment. That's why Lee Oswald killed President Kennedy. Oswald wanted a powerful voice to intervene for him, to save him from all of the empty days of his life that he was facing. But there was no saving for Oswald. Not when he was twelve. Not when he was old enough to kill Kennedy. Oswald was even denied a trial."

I listened in astonishment to Emerson. This was why Kennedy died!

"But now," Jenny said, "who could these people kill? They're not Oswalds."

"The killing of Kennedy was just the beginning. We're going to see more killing, more deaths, murder that isn't murder, not the way the FBI or the New York City police understand it," Emerson said. "It will be a killing of dead voices. Right now one fifth of all the murders are committed by children. We're seeing a new kind of killing and a new kind of murderer. Murderers like Oswald, murderers who look for the most logical victim. This happened in Germany in the 1920's when assassination gangs selected their most logical victims and then murdered them in the street, or in their homes, or the restaurants. The victims could never know they were being selected because there was no direct link between them and the assassination gangs. Harlem has already seen such murders. In Germany these assassination gangs began to rule the sidewalk. Their victims were people in government, leaders of labor organizations, business people, men easily identified but without immediate enemies, at least enemies they thought would murder them. The assassination gangs selected these men for murder because the members of the assassination gangs were men without jobs, they were the superfluous men in Germany after the end of World War I. These men roamed the streets and beer halls without a purpose until the idea of murder began to settle in their minds. Then for the first time since the end of the war they had a purpose, and that purpose was to murder whoever they felt was comfortable and in a position of power. Lee Oswald committed exactly this kind of murder. There must be fifty thousand kids in Harlem getting ready for this same kind of murdering, where the victim is no longer an individual and the murderer no longer has hope of becoming a person," Emerson said.

"It can happen," I said.

"It's already happening," Emerson said quietly.

70

"It *is* happening!" West cried out, his voice booming into the kitchen.

Standing in the doorway as he stood in a courtroom, tense, as though he himself were on trial, West said, "I didn't hear Emerson mention my idea of murder. We don't understand murder or crime. All the decisions of all the judges in the United States don't give us a single answer as to why the murder rate remains constant in the United States with a variation so slight from year to year that it seems as if all murders are planned a year ahead of time. Each year we have the same number of murders, eighty-five hundred. The number statistically hasn't changed since 1958. Why eighty-five hundred murders and not eighty-five thousand? Nobody knows. We only want to punish and protect property. That's the extent of our knowledge about crime, and all that we want to know. That's why we can't understand the murder of Kennedy and why we let his murder confuse us. In England children of eight and nine used to be hanged. The English have cut off the hands of children for theft. In America we don't hang children. But we send them to prison for ten years for an offense that would bring an adult only ten days in a city jail. We murder the minds of children, we murder the minds of a million children who come before the juvenile courts each year. This is what Emerson means when he says Oswald had no voice."

West moved into the kitchen, standing almost face to face with Emerson.

"But we haven't yet had in America a murder to startle

us," West said, "a murder to make us wonder, tremble before our ignorance. The murder of Kennedy might have been such a murder. But Kennedy's murder was wiped out by the glory of his funeral. Never was a man so swiftly destroyed. When the TV cameras followed Kennedy into a hole in the ground, he ceased to exist. Emerson is right. Kennedy was murdered, not assassinated. I think the reasons Emerson gives for the murder of Kennedy are absolutely correct even if there is no way of ever proving it. Lee Oswald is the new kind of murderer. Emerson is right."

Emerson moved back into the kitchen as West spoke, watching West as though he would spring on him like a leopard if he said a wrong word.

"Emerson knows murder," West said. "He's seen murder in the children he works with. We need a murder. I mean America needs a murder. Not a Leopold-Loeb case, which was sensational because it involved money, murder and homosexuality. We need a murder that will make us stand in awe of everything that we call justice. We need a murder committed by a man who knows why he is killing, why he is taking a human life, why he chooses to kill a man at a particular point in his life. A murder that threatens all of us, that alerts all of us at the same time. The ancient human sacrifices were such murders. The priests killed at an exact time to achieve an exact effect. We need a murder to open our eyes. A murder that forces us to open our eyes. The murder I might commit or that Brooks might commit or Emerson might commit if we believed that murder could

72

accomplish what we couldn't accomplish by law or logic."

West looked directly at Emerson. West said, "I've stopped looking for a preacher. I'm now looking for a murderer."

A WEEK AFTER THE PARTY I accepted Emerson's first invitation to visit his storefront church.

The first thing I saw was a magnificent wooden cross nailed to a whitewashed brick wall.

"A black boy of fifteen made that," Emerson said. "He sanded, polished, waxed and kept playing with the wood until it began to look like something. I let him nail it to the wall. But I think the cross would look more effective if the boy was put up alongside the cross."

"Why?"

"I knew you would ask me why. I don't know. Just that I think too many black people have been worshiping wrong. They concentrate too much on death. I'd like to see the young worshiped. We're probably the only special group of people in America who don't worship their young. I know, we dress them up in stiff nylon dresses and we stick bow ties on three-year-old boys and a father will get a garnishee for Easter clothes that he bought on 125th Street from some thieving bastard in a credit store. But that's not worshiping. You don't see black babies with faces that already know what it means to belong. That look escapes them. Black babies look cute, pop-eyed, full of wonder, as though they were invented by Amos and Andy. They don't have that intelligent, incisive look that I used to see at Yale. Those Yale kids weren't born with that look. That look is developed, it grows in a thousand different ways and no one way is enough, but you can see it in the W.A.S.P. babies before they're one year old."

"You've got your church here. You can start what you call the W.A.S.P. look here."

"I'm not just thinking of Harlem when I say that. I'm thinking of all those black families where the income is now over ten thousand dollars. The babies still look like they live on cornbread. You know that Harlem is dead and will stay dead unless some powerful builders decide to rip down these blocks the way they ripped down Third Avenue. It won't happen through this block-by-block social nonsense in Harlem. I just got a report from one of the block development projects. They got $150,000 to set up a block group. They bought off the addicts, so the addicts don't bother their blocks. The block workers hold group-therapy meetings to learn how they can relate to the poor. They wanted me to bring the church in. I told them no. The executive director said I was full of hostility. I told the executive director to go fuck himself, a phrase it took me twenty-one years to understand although I started using it when I was three."

"What do you do here?" I asked Emerson.

"We get the kids "released time" from school so that they know they have a place to go other than school. We let them sell raffle tickets. We try to show them white

75

people one day a week. The kids that have a brain left in their head we talk to. The others we try to get out of jail before they get a solid education in crime. We haven't lost a single kid yet to a training school. We had to practically threaten one judge with excommunication, but he let the kid go. She was a fourteen-year-old girl whose mother was trying to get her and her girl friends to hustle. For some reason the crazy judge thought the four-teen-year-old girl ought to be sent off to a state jail. We got the girl shipped off to an aunt in Alabama, but first we gave her what I call a five-minute psychiatric. I think it worked. Hang around. You'll see the kids come in for released time from school, which is religious time."

"Who's the minister?"

"We're waiting for a new one. The last one couldn't take the addicts on 115th Street. The addicts got on top of him from the first day. The crazy bastard passed out five-dollar bills like they had gone out of style. I came in early one morning when he didn't have a five-dollar bill. An addict had a knife against his throat. I bought his life back for five dollars. The crazy bastard actually went before the cross and thanked God for saving his life. Then he got out of here to really save it. The addicts can eat you up almost as much as the kids, who need more and more but who get less and less. Did West ever tell you how this church got started?"

"No."

"We lost him too, the minister who started this congregation. He was a white minister who came to New York from Connecticut. When he opened the doors for business, nobody showed up. The place was empty for days. Then he started walking around the block with candy in his pocket. He passed out candy for days. The kids began following him into the church for candy. Pretty soon he had a congregation, but only of children. No parents showed up. He didn't know what to pass out to bring in the parents. On Sunday these benches were filled with children. At first he was going to settle for a children's congregation. But then a few parents brought their children. They stayed long enough to give him a second look. His name was William Hall. It took him seven months, but he finally managed to get twenty-eight parents to show up on Sunday and about eight women to help the kids with trips, reading, spelling, math, everything else the billion-dollar educational sewer in this city is supposed to be doing. Then a fantastic thing happened. He began to realize that most of the children who went after the free candy were on welfare, which meant their parents were on welfare, and the people who weren't on welfare wouldn't associate with the welfare people. This caused a split in the congregation. Pretty soon he was running an adjunct of the welfare department, which happens to most of the groups in Harlem. But welfare was a bind for him. He couldn't penetrate into the secret world of welfare. He couldn't really believe that there exists a world where the only thing of value is failure, that the only thing that guarantees your success and survival is failure. This was too much for him. He tried talking to the people who ran the welfare department, but he quickly saw they were worse off than the people on welfare. They hated themselves. They hated the people on welfare. Those bastards just didn't care. Pretty soon he wasn't running a congregation, he was running a nineteenth-century poor farm. He saw that with all of the social laws on the books we were still in the nineteenth century, which was about as rotten a century as you can get. Hall was ready to throw himself under a subway car and make his peace with God. About a week before he left, two kids from a gang on West 114th Street cornered him. They said they were going to carve him up because he was a white prick. Hall didn't want to use violence on the kids, but neither did he want to get cut up by a couple of crazy kids. When they came screaming at him with knives in their hands, he had his belt ready. He beat them both to the ground and kept beating them until they dropped their knives.

"The addicts used to pound on his door at three, four in the morning, demanding money. He couldn't do anything for the pregnant girls of twelve and thirteen except see that the welfare department didn't starve them to death. Then one Sunday morning he decided to go, against his better judgment. But first he gave a magnificent sermon on welfare, saying how welfare would destroy people, ruin them by making them dependent, how welfare could turn your life and the life of your children and their children into one big expectancy of failure, and how once your life became a failure it became a bigger and bigger failure with high walls all around you and nobody could get over that kind of wall. It was a brilliant sermon. Right after this sermon William Hall was told to his face that he had no fucking right to talk that way in a church.

"We used to sit here on these benches, like we're doing now, and he would say to me, 'Now, what is right? I'm not expecting God to step in and resolve all this. I'm over that. I don't expect more than what I can do. But what can I do?' 'What do you want to do?' I would ask him. 'Go skiing in Vermont,' he would say. 'Then go,' I would say to him, 'because you're powerless here.' He didn't like that. After a while he began to hate me. Every time he wanted to make a move, I told him it wouldn't work."

Emerson smiled, not a mocking smile but a tired smile for having talked so long.

"How many times have you heard this talk about Harlem?" Emerson said.

"I like your William Hall. What did he finally find out about his little parish?"

"That he was useless. That something was destroying the lives of these children that he couldn't comprehend. The worst thing that can happen to a man is to make a mistake and to know that he has made a mistake. Hall didn't make any mistakes. It's just that with all of his good will he was useless."

Emerson opened the door leading to his cramped office. "This is where God's work is done." Emerson pointed to a mimeographing machine and a pile of comic books.

"What time do the kids come in?"

"You mean the monsters. They'll be running in here out of the schools on these blocks."

"Why didn't Hall actually start a children's congregation? It might have worked."

"It was phony. It couldn't work. *Life* Magazine or *Look* might have taken some more pictures of little black bastards sitting in the pews, and that would have been the end of it. These little black monsters don't need God. They've got God."

"Why do you call them monsters?"

"You don't think these are children here in Harlem? Some of them, yes. But the rest are monsters. They're children when they're born, but within six months they're dead. They stay dead until they die."

The monsters came into Emerson's office without knocking, six of them followed by three more monsters. They grabbed at the comic books piled on Emerson's desk. They didn't look at me. They went to the file cabinet and took out two balls and a bat, a big round ball and a plastic pinball game. They all looked about ten years old. The boys wore white shirts. The girls hung around Emerson, touching him, picking up papers on his desk so that he would slap at their hands. Their bodies were like the bodies of puppies, wanting warmth, to be touched, handled, to brush up against something alive. Their hands were all over Emerson. Six more monsters entered the office. Emerson got up. The monsters were shouting, begging for Emerson's attention.

"You've got to quiet down," Emerson called out. "Can't you see that I have a visitor?"

But I wasn't a visitor. I was an intrusion. The yelling died down. Emerson went to a bookshelf and started passing out coloring books.

"Take these into the other room. I'll be there soon."

One little monster didn't leave the office. He was a boy of about ten. He hung on to Emerson, touching him, until Emerson placed him in a chair by the bookshelf. The boy got up from the chair and came back to Emerson.

"This is Mr. Brooks," Emerson said to the boy, "say hello to him."

"Hello," I said to the boy.

"Hello," he said, in a quiet far-off voice, not seeing me, turning his attention immediately to Emerson.

"All right," Emerson told the boy, "you go into the other room too and I'll be there."

"You're sure?" the boy said, hesitating, as though the door might close on him forever.

"I'm sure."

Emerson closed the door on the shrieking monsters.

"They're only yelling because you're here. I guess you picked up that they feel you're an intrusion."

"They couldn't make it more obvious."

"These little bastards have an absolute instinct for the preservation of failure. They can tune in threats. They can smell out teachers, principals, the law, everybody who they think can guess their ignorance. That's why they can't be touched. Their ignorance means their survival. They're used to succeeding in failure. That little eight-year-old boy that just left can't read a line of the language he speaks, he can only count up to seven, and he doesn't know his colors. He has never seen his father and he never will."

"Don't they get God and a Father here?"

"They just get me and I'm no god. You know that I can't touch what goes on outside of this storefront. This is Harlem, the drug addicts, the stopped-up toilets, the rats, the screaming mothers, the murder, the noise; this is permanent. These kids know I'm only temporary. A prop. When Hall was here they didn't even notice me. The minute Hall left they started sucking on me. When I go they'll start sucking on the new one."

"What does West say to you about all this?"

"West is in a bind. The law he's involved with is more conservative than education. The more they both change, the more they remain the same. Now West is hung up on murder. He sees the last seventy years as one great big blood bath. West thinks we have to solve the problem of crime. He thinks that comes first, before any other kind of change is possible. I don't see change and I don't expect change.

"Once you get out of New York City you begin to see what I call the invisible people. That's because the only people they want to see are themselves, and everyone else frightens them. The invisible people own America. They get the goodies. You can't touch these people. Nothing touches them. You can get a handful of nuts involved in demonstrations, you can get some priests marching, but that doesn't change anything, not for real. That's why S. T. West wants a murderer and a victim. But it took thirty-two years to kill Trujillo. And nobody in Germany could kill Hitler. Not a single Russian got a bullet into Stalin. Not a single Italian could kill Mussolini, not until his death didn't mean anything. Yet a frightened boy with a secondhand rifle could kill Kennedy in a moving car with two shots from a mail-order gun. Now, there was a murderer and a victim. And what did it mean to the invisible country? It meant a five-hour spectacle on TV—all that show, with the horses and the boots and the drums and bagpipes, didn't tell America why Kennedy died. His funeral was wasted. His death was wasted. Kennedy died because Oswald needed somebody to love him, to recognize him, to speak to him, just the way you see these monsters here in the church need recognition to live. The way Kennedy with all of his power recognized that Yale professor held by the Russians and got him freed six days before Oswald murdered Kennedy."

The monsters started knocking on the door. One of the monsters was crying.

"Mr. Emerson, Mr. Emerson!"

Emerson got up and opened the door. The eight-year-old boy was crying. He said, "You said you were coming out!"

"All right," Emerson said, "I'm coming out now." Emerson said to me, "This is story time now. I don't think the kids will mind if you sit in."

The children had arranged their chairs in a big half-circle. Emerson asked the oldest boy to get me a chair and I joined the circle.

"Who's the storyteller today?" Emerson asked.

A girl raised her hand.

"You then, Della, you're going to tell us a story to-day?"

"Yes, Mr. Emerson."

"All right, Della, any time you want to begin."

I saw Della glance in my direction and I half raised myself to leave the circle, to let Della tell her story, but Emerson put his hand on my arm and I sat down again. Della edged toward the front of her chair. She looked about twelve. She wore a cotton skirt and a white blouse. She was thin, her knees bony. Her eyes turned on me again. I saw she was trying to swallow me in and I could only sit still and hope that my presence wouldn't ruin her story.

"My name is Della Roberts. The name of my story is 'The Squirrely Squirrel.' " Her voice trembled at the first words, but when she said "squirrely squirrel" the children laughed and she was on her way into her story.

"One day I heard about a squirrel that lives in Morningside Park. His name is the Squirrely Squirrel. I saw him two days ago. He is brown. I gave him a bag of potato chips, but he likes popcorn. He has a lot of relatives living in the park and in Central Park. The Squirrely Squirrel is the favorite squirrel in all the parks because he likes to make visits and bring presents. He brings peanuts to his cousin in Central Park. He has one relative who only eats Cracker Jack. One day the Squirrel decided to visit his cousin in Riverside Park. The traffic was very bad on Broadway. The Squirrely Squirrel usually liked to stop in a drugstore and buy some cheese popcorn for his

84

cousin in Riverside Park, but this morning he had no money. He looked for something to bring his cousin, but he could only find old Superman books, which he took with him. The squirrels, you know, are the only wild animals left in New York. All the other wild animals are gone, which is why the Squirrely Squirrel likes to visit his relatives. When he got to Riverside Park after many adventures trying to cross the West Side Highway, the Squirrely Squirrel found his cousin Albert sleeping in his favorite tree. Wake up, said the Squirrely Squirrel, it's me. It's who? said Cousin Albert. It's me, said the Squirrely Squirrel. You, said Cousin Albert, why didn't you say so? What did you bring me? Nothing but some old Superman books. Well, said Cousin Albert, don't just stand there, climb up the tree. The Squirrely Squirrel climbed up the tree and found his Cousin Albert in bed. Do you always sleep? asked the Squirrely Squirrel. No, said Cousin Albert, not when I'm awake. The two squirrels decided to have some fun and they went to the park, where the children were eating ice cream. They went to beg for food from the children eating peanuts. Cousin Albert even tried to eat an apple. They saw an airplane in the sky. It had big wings that flew around and around like a bird. The Squirrely Squirrel and his Cousin Albert rushed to climb the tallest tree they could find to see the strange airplane. If I could fly like that, I wouldn't walk, said Cousin Albert. You're always sleeping, so you don't have to worry, said the Squirrely Squirrel. The strange airplane came closer and closer to the top of the tree. Cousin Albert yelled out, Watch out or you'll fall. No, I won't, said the Squirrely Squirrel, I'm going to fly, I'm going to reach into the airplane, here it comes for me, here it comes! The airplane came closer and closer and when it was just over the top of the tree, the wings reached out and brought the Squirrely Squirrel into the airplane and he flew around the world before it was time to go home for supper, where he had no one to eat with again."

WHEN THE MONSTERS FINISHED their released time, Emerson asked me to come back into his office. "Are you free for about another hour?" he asked. "I've got something up in my room I'd like you to have. I live about five blocks from here."

Emerson lived on West 117th Street off Lenox. His building had an elevator, but it wasn't running. We had to walk up six flights. Emerson didn't speak as we started the climb. Nor had he spoken much as we walked from the church. He had not commented on the girl's story. He had walked silently and I had kept silent with him. His building looked as if it had been gutted by a fire. The mailboxes were smashed. The lock on the front door was pulled out. The telephone in the hallway was pulled out of the wall. There was a huge mirror in the lobby. I saw Emerson reflected in eight pieces in the broken mirror. The walls of the lobby were smeared with chalk writing. Children seemed to be running out of the walls. I expected rats to be crawling on the ceiling. The marble on the stairway was worn away. The windows on the stairway landings were broken, covered with chicken wire, the soot piled up. The walls on the stairway landing were scribbled with chalk, the chalk dug into the walls. The scribbling was hysterical, the names of children, the monsters, the half-dozen curse words known to everyone. The building felt wet, as though it had sunk into a cave. The stairway got narrower as we got higher. The blue-white light of television screens was visible through the doors opened for air. When we got to the top floor Emerson's shirt was wet and my hands were black from the railing. Emerson opened the two locks and I heard the police lock scraping against the floor.

"I took it because of the view," Emerson said as he pushed open the door on his white-walled room, bare except for two travel posters, a desk with a typewriter, a telephone and a bed covered with a Madras throw.

"Here it is, the view."

Emerson opened his windows and there in front of us was Harlem, pushed together in one solid mass of steaming tar, the black chimneys spouting up. There was no escape for the eye; you had to see what the builders of the twentieth century had erected, a pit, built with no design but contempt.

Emerson went to his desk and took out a nine-by-twelve envelope.

"I want you to take this," Emerson said, "with no more explanation than that I want you to take it now. Take it now and I'll get it back later. I'll walk you down. Some son of a bitch in this building might throw you out of a window for the change you've got in your pocket."

When I got back to my desk on the thirty-fifth floor I opened Emerson's nine-by-twelve envelope. He had told me what to expect in it when I left him on the corner of West 125th Street. "I just started talking one night," Emerson said, "and this came out. Don't try to make too much out of it."

I took out the tape coiled around eighteen hundred feet of Emerson's voice and inserted it into the recorder on my desk. I heard Emerson's voice come through, saying, "Testing, testing, testing," and then Emerson's voice was cut off. I let the tape run soundlessly for ten minutes, fifteen minutes, and as the coil of tape unwound, I heard a cough, a window opening, water running in a sink, a window slamming shut, a voice coming up from the street, the phone ringing, six rings and then silence. Finally Emerson's voice came back on the tape.

"What am I testing?" The voice was startled, as though the sea were flinging his words back at him.

"I am testing what I just saw. I was sitting here by the window and I saw a baby go hurtling through the air. A black baby. There is no other kind around here." There was a pause in the tape, a whirling of the tape. This wasn't Emerson's storefront-church voice, nor his door-greeting voice at West's party, but a voice white people hear only by accident—sometimes in a subway or turning a street corner in Harlem. It is never directed at them, but away from them. This voice more than all the history books tells how the white man and the black man are separated in America.

Emerson's voice came back on the tape. "I've heard of babies being found in furnaces, garbage cans, the gutter, on stoops, and I've heard of babies thrown off roofs.

89

Now I've seen one. A black baby thrown out of a window, because it was too little to climb to the window sill and fall. It's now in the street. In the middle of West 117th Street. But so far I haven't heard any sirens. Yet somebody other than me must have seen the baby. There must be somebody down there on the street. Everybody didn't run and hide when they saw the baby flying at them. I heard voices in the street. I heard the boys in the street yelling fuck you, fuck you, which is a phrase that taunts us to produce another human being as crazy as ourselves. But I don't hear them yelling now. The sirens ought to be sounding now. The police must be coming. That red circling light will be going around and around and everybody will be hiding in the doorways, looking to see without being seen. That baby can't be there alone on the sidewalk now. Will its mother run down the six flights? It had to be from a seventh-floor window. I was looking out of the window, just looking, the way I look, as though the bomb might go off and I want a chance to see the mushroom cloud. Should I go down to the street? What could I say to the dead baby? The dead mother, what's she doing now? Looking out of the window? Finishing her supper? Watching TV? Hiding under a bedsheet? Running through the streets tearing her hair? Vomiting in the toilet? Walking crazy around her three rooms? What do you do after you throw your baby out of a window? How do you start living again? What's the first thing you do? Try to fly after the baby? Try to catch it in mid-air? Try to bring it back up to life? In the morning maybe I can ask the mother just what she did after she threw her baby out of the window. The sirens should be here by now. I told the desk sergeant I saw a baby just thrown out of the window on West 117th Street. What? he said. I repeated, I saw a baby thrown out of the window on West 117th Street. Is the baby dead? he said. I don't know, I said. All right, he said, there'll be a squad car there in a minute. The minute won't find the baby alive. What am I testing? This recorder was just here on my desk as I saw the baby going by. What was I going to record? Not the death of a baby thrown out of a window. I was going to record a speech by President Kennedy to play at the church on Sunday because we have no minister and some of the people still show up and they'll listen to Kennedy because he can't hurt them."

The sirens came on, a roaring noise, and Emerson said, "Now everybody knows what to do."

AFTER THE TAPE I invited Emerson to the Friday lunch at the Foundation. Emerson couldn't get more sick to his stomach at the lunch than I had listening to his fantastic tape recording. The Friday lunch came at the end of the month. The guest was Phillip Green, who had just been handed $2,500,000 by the Federal government to start a Youth Development Corps in Cleveland, Ohio.

Emerson had a fantastic insight into the murder of Kennedy, a fantastic and dangerous insight. A new kind of murderer and a new kind of murder, and perhaps Emerson would be able to identify both. From what Emerson said, there was no need to identify the victim, it could be any name out of the telephone book.

Emerson stood by the huge windows in my office looking out on the splendor and spectacle of Fifth Avenue. "It's dazzling," Emerson said. "Dazzling. This insane city is plain dazzling. This city can soak up 100,000 drug addicts, 675,000 people on welfare, 100,000 unemployed black kids in Harlem, one million apartments unfit for any kind of human habitation, the filthiest air in the world, and still look dazzling."

"From thirty-five stories up, even Harlem would look like Paris," I said. "Let me give you a rundown on the lunch. The Foundation has its own dining room. It's down the hall from here. Charles Eaton had the dining room and kitchen built. He thought the experts would be more intimidated and become more expansive eating in a private dining room. Eaton was right. It's the best investment the Foundation has made. Eaton uses the dining room for Friday lunches to pick brains. He invites an expert like Green and about ten other people to ask the questions. The expert seldom has time to eat. A lot of solid information passes through the two-hour lunch. The guest list for today is Robert Fellows, he's an authority on public housing. Dr. Hodes will be the only woman here, she's a psychiatrist who specializes in children. Dr. Masters will be here, he's one of the few sociologists in America with a public reputation, the rest of the sociologists don't dare risk their reputations in public. Edman will be here. You might have run into him, he's running a block-development project in East Harlem. The famous Dr. Bird from Harvard will be here. Bird startled everyone a year ago by saying that all pregnancies in Negro families where the income is less than $3,500 a year should be aborted. Frost will be here. He's a lawyer who acts as though he has a first mortgage on the United States. He and West are old friends."

"Am I supposed to ask questions?" Emerson asked.

"If you want to."

"Does this Green know anything?" Emerson asked. "Because I'm willing to learn."

"Let's go in and find out." We went down the book-lined corridor, into the dining room.

When we were all introduced and assembled, Charles Eaton stood up and said, "Let me begin by saying that this is the age of the tape recorder. But we don't record these lunches. We don't take notes. I call these lunches from time to time to have the Foundation take an intimate look at problems that we're interested in. One of the most puzzling problems everywhere, considering the time, money, research, effort, and years of discussion given to it, is juvenile delinquency. Which I'm inclined to think is adult delinquency, but saying that doesn't solve anything. Except it's probably the reason why we have so much trouble getting a sensible appraisal of delinquency. We prefer to be ignorant of our own ignorance. I think it's going to take a long time to exhaust our present store of ignorance." Eaton pressed his foot on the floor buzzer to alert the kitchen to serve the first course.

"Phillip Green is now involved in a $2½ million delinquency-control program in Cleveland, Ohio. We don't have formal speeches here, but we do ask people with the authority of Mr. Green to start us off."

Mr. Wharton, the waiter, came in with a tray of shrimp.

"From the sea comes all of our knowledge," Green said, and he got a polite laugh.

Emerson ignored the shrimp and fixed his eyes on Green.

"I suppose you all feel the impatience I feel whenever anyone starts to talk about delinquency," Green said,

94

picking up from Eaton. "It is puzzling. It is a blindness. But so is everything we do in the human sciences, and we shouldn't expect miracles in the field of delinquency, where you work with children, children who through no fault of their own find themselves criminals at the age of eight, nine, ten years. More than half of all the delinquents are delinquent before the age of ten. Delinquency, real delinquency, means a jail sentence." Green coughed and continued.

"Today at least one million children a year are brought before the three thousand juvenile-court judges in the United States. Strictly speaking, these aren't juvenile courts. They are criminal courts, for the child is usually being tried for a criminal offense and he can be deprived of his liberty. Regardless of the sentence, his appearance in a juvenile court, whether guilty or not, can ruin a child for life. A juvenile-court conviction—the juvenile-court judges prefer to call their convictions 'findings'—can keep a boy out of the Army, out of the civil service, out of some colleges, out of a lot of jobs. His conviction has more impact than any other prison sentence except the death penalty. I think the single most important thing that we have to recognize about juvenile delinquency is the vicious system of justice that we have developed for children. In actual practice, children suffer more harm from the juvenile court than any other institution they will encounter during their lifetime." Green paused, as though to sound out agreement on what he had said. The silence forced him to continue. I think we were all waiting for accountability, accountability for the $2½ million.

"The juvenile courts originated in 1899 in Chicago as a revulsion that set in against the then current practice of sending children of eight and nine to prison with adult offenders. But we still do it! There must be fifty thousand children right now in the United States who are being detained in adult prisons because the local counties, towns, cities, do not have adequate facilities for the detention of children.

"The juvenile-court judge sits as judge, prosecutor, defense attorney, guardian of the child and enemy of the child. The juvenile-court judges are charged by society to be brilliant, compassionate, fatherly, just and wise, way beyond their capacity. They have sent children to jail on evidence that wouldn't have convicted a witch at Salem. The juvenile-court judge is supreme in his court, but in most instances he is a supreme idiot. In some jurisdictions he has to listen to fifty cases a day. Right here in New York City a judge often hears thirty-five cases a day. This is enough to make a supreme idiot out of any man or woman. No judge can operate with any dignity in this kind of system. He must cut short the lives of the children who come before him and silently say to himself, These bastards are doomed whatever I do, so get on with the docket. The docket must be cleared! Occasionally a judge will stop the treadmill when a case comes up that forces his interest or that haunts him. The real control of delinquency is tied up with the kind of legal attention the child gets when he enters the courtroom, because from that time on he is an official delinquent, and as matters now stand, we do everything that is legally pos-

sible to make certain that the child will remain a delinquent until he dies."

Frost, who used to volunteer some of his legal time to
help S. T. West in his law office on 116th Street, gave
Green a chance to eat some shrimp. Frost said, "A lot of
judges that I know in New York City would agree with
you. I've talked with enough judges after their day in
court to see them baffled by their decisions and the strain
of the decisions they have to make in the juvenile court.
We give a special status to a judge which is beyond the
capacity of most judges to maintain. Judges are powerful
in court. There is no question of it. Not even the gang-
ster period in American life, when judges were bought
and sold, could mar the luster of a judge. One person has
to become our moment of certainty. This is the judge. He
has to make the decision. I can see how an ignorant judge
in a juvenile court can be devastating to children. He has
to protect his ignorance by doing what he thinks the majority of his community wants done with a bunch of poor
whites, poor blacks, poor Mexicans, poor Puerto Ricans,
poor Indians, because these are the children who come
into the juvenile courts. The middle-class child never sees
the juvenile court unless he commits a crime that can't
be explained away. The ignorant judge has to respond to
the mob opinion, and he does exactly this. He convicts
most of the offenders who come before him. He locks
them up in jails. What alternative does an intelligent
judge have?

"How can a judge with sensitivity send a child either
to prison or back into the environment that he knows is

destroying the child? The child is under the protection of the court, of the entire land, from the moment a petition is drawn up. New York City probably has some of the best juvenile-court judges in the country, yet the New York judges are tied to a stake. In New York City a judge can't make what he might consider a wise or just decision for a child. He can't send a child to a warm, therapeutic institution that has been recommended by a psychologist, because there aren't any warm, therapeutic institutions. A New York judge doesn't have the authority to send a child to an institution, because the institution has to agree to accept the child. And the institutions in New York won't accept any child that they feel is a threat to them. This means that a child who has emotional problems, arson problems, sexual problems—exactly the kind of child who needs serious institutional help—can't get it. A great many children wind up in prisons, jails, reform schools, training schools, detention centers, simply because there aren't enough facilities, let alone facilities that can be of decent help to them. So the judge in a juvenile court has become a frustrated bureaucrat whom we pay $25,000 a year, whom we load with status and honor, and to whom we say: We will not give you proper institutions for the children, we will not give you a trained probation staff, we will not give you adequate medical and psychiatric facilities, we will not even give you time to read the prepared recommendations and case studies of the children who come up before you for sentencing. We only want you to punish children, to keep them dependent and frightened. If you want an idea of what I mean, take a trip in New York City to the juvenile court on Union Hall Street, which disgraces the judges and the children who appear in it."

Green said, "I didn't mean to lay the ax on the judges, just as I wouldn't attack the psychiatrists in a state training school for the emotional problems of the children they have to work with. But I started out by talking about the control of delinquency. The court is the first control point to check out, because a child isn't a delinquent until he appears in court. I think we have been fooled by what the courts could do. Or maybe Mr. Frost is right and we never intended the courts to be effective. If this is so, then we have set up an elaborate billion-dollar facility to keep up a façade."

"Have you or anyone else worked out an alternative to the juvenile-court system?" Edman asked. I couldn't tell if Emerson recognized Edman from East Harlem. Emerson studied the faces around the table. Dr. Julia Hodes smiled professionally at Emerson, a smile he didn't return.

"What alternative would you want for the court system now in effect for children?" Hodes asked.

"None!" Green said. "Because we have no alternative. Our whole investment is in the juvenile-court system." Green pushed aside his bowl of iced shrimp. "I don't want to put the judges on the rack. The judge is a funnel. What I am saying is that the juvenile court is where we have deposited all of our ignorance and fear toward dependent children, most of whom are Negro. Some of the judges would like to be bailed out of their present hope-

lessness. Some prefer it this way. But the judges are powerless to effect change. What has paralyzed the court is
urban filth, and this filth has eaten its way into the courtroom.

"No, whatever the judges are, they usually aren't fools.
They can read. Most actually read the probation reports.
They see a similarity in all of the reports they read. They
see a pattern emerging that is bigger than the specific
pattern of any one child, but this pattern always destroys
a specific child. The specific pattern is a child on welfare
or an environment similar to welfare, a child who has no
father and who has a mother who can't take care of him.
A child destroyed from the moment of his birth. He is a
new breed of child. He is the new poverty. He needs new
ways of help, not the old ways of hurting him."

Eaton pressed the silent buzzer. The shrimp bowls
were cleared away. Mr. Wharton brought out three bottles of Beaujolais.

"If the judges aren't the villains, then who are the villains?" Charles Eaton asked Phillip Green.

"Dr. Masters ought to be able to answer that question,
if he agrees there is a villain," Green said.

Emerson picked up his wineglass and studied Masters.
Masters glanced toward Emerson as though acknowledg-
ing Emerson's appraisal of him.

"I don't think it makes any sense to talk about villains," Dr. Masters said in his quiet professorial voice, a
voice that had startled several Congressional committees
because of his insistence on speaking honestly about
what he called the external reality. "It's too simple to

find villains, and impossible to convince the villains that they are doing anything wrong or that they should change to suit somebody else's notions about their behavior. It's too simple-minded to state that bit of wisdom that strikes every undergraduate in his first year, the wisdom that says we're all guilty—all villains. There are degrees of villainy and guilt. The least guilty are the people for whom none of this is of any concern. They can go through their entire lives without ever speaking to a judge, a detective, a social worker, a psychiatrist. There is an old social-psychology trick of having the first-year students write down all the acts they committed as children that were delinquent acts. In Wilton, Connecticut, when I was ten years old, I broke a window with a baseball. Nothing happened. My father paid for the window. Yet there are documented cases of children today being sentenced to eight and ten years in training schools for similar offenses, for this so-called delinquent act. The acts which we call delinquent and for which a child can be sent to prison are so vague, so multitudinous, that any act can be considered delinquent if the court wants to do so.

"Real delinquency is a special world for special children who have been isolated from the protection of adults for the whole of their lives.

"For seventy-five years we have been developing and training special groups of people to work with these children. These are the people who have failed the delinquent child. They have failed to make clear that the delinquent child is a special child and that he needs special protection. I think that the recent attempts to deal with this problem, such as Mobilization For Youth and, if Mr. Green will excuse me, the Youth Development Corps, are fraudulent attempts to work with the delinquent child. The truth is that we don't want to help the delinquent child. We want to punish him. These children have become the symbol of our own self-hate. That is why we are willing to invest billions of dollars in institutions, courts, jails and high-sounding programs for these children, without expecting a penny's return on this investment, without seriously expecting a single life to be changed. A father in Scarsdale spends $4,000 a year for his son's education at Harvard and he expects him to be a lawyer. We spend $5,000 a year to keep a child in a state training school and we expect him to be a criminal. No one is shocked by this."

Mr. Wharton brought out the main dish, chicken breast with a thick yellow mayonnaise sauce, which no one looked at. From thirty-five stories below, the sound traveling upward from Fifth Avenue, came the howling of fire engines, the braying, shattering horns developed by the New York City Fire Department so that the air-raid sirens, if they ever go off, won't be confused with isolated fires.

"I find that noise," Charles Eaton said, "the ugliest sound in New York, but a necessary sound. Tell me, Dr. Masters, you say no one is shocked; why is no one shocked?"

"Your trouble, Mr. Eaton, is that you have no professional bias to screen out your failures. If you were a social psychologist, a public-welfare worker, a teacher in a Harlem school, a probation worker in the family court, a priest, a judge in the juvenile-term court, a deputy director of the Office of Economic Opportunity or even Mr. Shriver himself, who after all has been delegated our conscience in these matters, you wouldn't see these problems as failures but as complexities. And you would be kept endlessly busy telling yourself that the complexities are as important as the problem itself, if not more important. To put it another way, when a disturbed child enters an institution, he must conform to the institution; the institution doesn't conform to the child. In this way the institution always wins and the child always loses."

"Masters is absolutely right!" Dr. Bird, from Harvard, cried out. "Take the welfare workers in this country. They see nothing, they do nothing and they say nothing! If they opened their eyes for a minute, they would burn down the welfare centers here in New York. But they go home to sleep every night like efficient hangmen. The fantastic psychological horror is that these welfare workers understand none of the horror surrounding them. That's your answer, Eaton. The welfare workers in this country are the best example of why no reverse is possible in the way we think about dependent people, particularly dependent children. The welfare workers actually have the least to lose and the most to gain from opening their mouths and eyes and yelling at the top of their voices about the horror they see. They aren't as hardened, as conditioned, as rotten, as the other professionals in this field. But they remain silent. Think of it for a minute.

Think of all of the thousands of educated people who have gone through the welfare mills of New York, Chicago, Los Angeles, Philadelphia, and only two or three people have written about their experiences. The only real piece of work was done by John Brooks here. The rest has been a lot of sloppy sentimental nonsense, horrifying lies and a horror to the people who have any familiarity with the truth of what actually goes on under the name of welfare.

"In welfare you have a government organization with absolute documentation of the problems we're talking about. But those sons of bitches maintain a silence that makes the rest of us look like guilt-ridden psychopaths. You don't need a Youth Development Corps in Cleveland, Ohio, Mr. Green; you need a welfare department that knows what the hell they are doing, why they are doing what they do, that has a sense of aspiration about the people they're working with. Anything else is nonsense. The courts, the jails, none of it will operate with any degree of sanity until we resolve what we mean by welfare and until we come to an understanding of what the new world of welfare is all about. Do you know what I would do with that $2½ million those idiots in Washington gave to you to make their own consciences look clean? I would use that money to buy five hundred college degrees for five hundred kids out of fifty thousand that I could save, just the way I used my own money to buy three college degrees for my own three children."

Green drank his wine in a gulp. "Nobody is absolutely right," Green said, "not Dr. Masters, not even the learned professor from Harvard. We're working with a population that has been buried underground for a hundred years. The Negro population in this country, for all of its middle-class pretense, is an underground population. We know more about the Red Chinese than we know about the Negroes in America. We don't believe the Negro can ever be white—that's the extent of our knowledge. So how can you expect the people who administer public welfare on a local level to behave any differently? We need real knowledge, gut knowledge, Dr. Bird and Dr. Masters, and you only get this knowledge by working in black neighborhoods, teaching in black schools, by exposure. Because there isn't a person in this room who couldn't recite ten homemade commandments for being kind to black Americans and raising the standards of black children."

Dr. Masters said quietly, patiently, like a teacher to his pupil, "You haven't told us yet what you intend to do with the $2½ million grant Washington gave to you."

"Nobody asked me!" Green said sharply. "Do you know that since the Federal government recognized the existence of the slum child, as the newspapers so romantically refer to these children—I think of them as dehumanized living organisms—the Federal government has approved 18,500 individual projects for these children at a cost of $1 billion under Title I of the Elementary and Secondary Education Act. This is $1 billion! What could $1 billion buy, Dr. Bird? It could probably buy Harvard lock, stock, library and brains. Has the $1 billion bought brains for the so-called slum children? These programs

are too diffuse, too inept, too tangled in existing preju-
dices to get to the exact child the $1 billion is supposed
to reach. The 18,500 projects are 18,500 wasted projects.
Most of the 18,500 projects are run according to the pre-
vailing notion that all these kids need is just a little bit
more attention, a few more trips to the art museum,
more paints and brushes, Shakespeare played in the park,
and then we'll be off the hook as far as they are concerned. No, Dr. Bird, your welfare workers can't handle
this problem, although I agree with you that they have
absolute entry into the homes of these children and that
they control a $12 billion purse string. The welfare work-
ers alone can't fight the system of welfare we have developed."

"You still haven't said what your $2½ million will buy
in Cleveland, Ohio," Dr. Bird said.

"How do I know what it will buy?" Green said, his
voice rising for the first time. "I have a commitment to
go into Cleveland and to do what I can for fifty thousand
black children. I'm taking on the responsibility!" And for
the first time Green looked directly at Emerson for support.

"What specifically will you do in Cleveland?" Dr. Bird
asked again.

"Specifically," Green said, trying to reach for irony,
trying to put the professors back into their classrooms, "I
will go into Cleveland, Ohio, and waste $2½ million of
the taxpayers' money on roughly fifty thousand black children who live in a neighborhood that makes Harlem look
like Sutton Place. I will make an attempt to get these

black children to burn to the ground every slum building, murder every welfare worker who doesn't send them an adequate allowance for school clothing, murder every teacher who talks about the black kids being dumber than monkeys, murder every cop who brutalizes a black boy just to keep him under control, murder every social worker who goes off to conferences in Atlantic City and who never sets foot in the black neighborhoods of Cleveland, murder every middle-class Negro in Cleveland who won't get out of his $30,000 home to show the black kids how he got his $30,000 home, and even murder me, if they feel it's justified. Does that satisfy you, Dr. Bird, or would you like me to dump them all on Harvard?"

"Not quite enough," Dr. Bird said. "Because in their own way the children are already doing this. They have murdered and raped social workers. They have destroyed buildings. They have destroyed whatever comfort the Negroes in their $30,000 homes may derive from their $30,000 homes."

"What would you like me to do, Professor Bird," Green finally said, "since you are obviously baiting me with questions from a position of yours that isn't clear to me?"

No one looked at the chicken breast smeared with yellow mayonnaise sauce. The little round potatoes with parsley lay cold, uneaten.

"Not you, Mr. Green," Dr. Bird said, "but Washington, D.C. I read your 250-page proposal for the Youth Development Corps and it reads exactly like every other proposal Washington has asked me to read, although I think Mobilization For Youth here in New York City writes longer, more high-blown, improbable prose. The spending of money has to be justified. We have developed overnight a marvelous jargon for this justification. The jargon is unassailable because there is a bond of ignorance between the people in Washington who pass out the money and the people who spend the money. These two form a link that no black child, no black neighborhood, no individual, can touch. That's why every project of this kind has been a failure, and that is why your project will be a failure. After spending over $1 million during a five-year study, a project in Syracuse, New York, came to the incredible conclusion that delinquency is caused by exposure to bad neighborhoods and that bad neighborhoods are bad for bad children. They actually wrote this in a glossy brochure that must have used up $100,000 of the grant money. My graduate students laughed over the report. You should hear their comments on the progress report Mobilization For Youth issued in 1963."

"Then what do you propose?" Green called out.

"This is what I would do, Mr. Green," Dr. Bird said. "I would put an end to all demonstration programs that only demonstrate our ignorance. I would stop giving absurd sums of money to universities and social agencies for social research. Most of this stuff isn't research, but a cheap way of buying our consciences clean. I would put an end to all of the agencies that have multiplied in Washington and outside of Washington, that exist solely on the bounty of Washington and that never get through to children. I would close all institutions for children that have a capacity of more than twenty-five children. I would close all training schools and prisons for children. Your target population is in welfare, and that's where the best people, money, brains, authority, have to be. I would send Mr. Sargent Shriver back to the Merchandise Mart in Chicago. I think he would make an excellent chairman for a board of managers for a big local charity, but he hasn't the faintest idea of what to do in a field where he is now the primary spokesman. Mr. Shriver has completely dehumanized poverty by making it respectable. This is what I would do, Mr. Green. You still haven't told us what you intend to do with $2½ million in Cleveland, Ohio."

Phillip Green turned sharply to Emerson. Everyone at the table stared at Emerson. Suddenly Emerson's presence dominated the dining room, but only because his skin was black. In the silence you could hear the far-off street sounds, the automobile horns, the movement of ten million people in the streets, the opening and shutting of millions of file drawers.

Phillip Green faced Emerson and said, "Mr. Emerson, if you were given $2½ million to help fifty thousand black children, what would you do?"

Emerson quietly said, "I would take the $2½ million, put it into a neat pile and burn it." And then he smiled at Green.

If I were Green, the smile would haunt me for the rest of my life. But neither had I entered into a pact with Emerson to be absolved, the absolution we crave from a Negro friend when we feel we know him, the absolution that is never given, because to expect absolution means you haven't been absolved. The other faces around the table looked as if they were going to vomit the breast of chicken with the yellow mayonnaise sauce. There was an instant silence, a silence that forced each one of us around the table to say to himself what he or she really thought about the existence of the Negro in America, an existence that would someday stagger the belief of the world. This is what I thought, for the record: The black man in America always had to assume the white man was human. Because everything in existence said the white man was human. If not human in 1791, then in the 1820's; if not the 1820's, then with the death of Lincoln; if not human then, then in the 1900's: and if still not human, then in the First War; and if not in the First War, then in the peace that followed. Certainly in the Depression! And if the Depression was not to be it, then in the next war, and if not in the next war, then the uneasy peace that followed, or in the wars that followed the peace, or now, sometime now, when everything in print, in law, in existence, said the white man was human.

In desperation at the silence that surrounded him, Phillip Green cried out to Emerson, "You still didn't answer my question!"

"He did!" Dr. Masters said. "He did for me! Let me tell you a story from history, Mr. Green. This is about Gandhi. During a period of unbelievable famine in India when millions of villagers were dying from starvation, the British government sent a bunch of envoys to Gandhi with sacks full of grain. Gandhi took the sacks full of British grain, threw them into a pile and then burned them. Only the pacifism of Gandhi kept him from burning the envoys."

I TOOK A SEAT in the last row of the courtroom. The courtroom was empty except for a couple of spectators up front. S. T. West had asked me to come to Foley Square. I watched him as he sat at a long table, a yellow legal pad in front of him. The jury looked asleep. The judge kept staring at Robert Sims, who had murdered a grocer on 98th Street near Madison Avenue. S. T. West told me the judge lived at 95th and Madison Avenue and he would hang Sims if he could. The district attorney was questioning a witness, but I couldn't hear a word they said. I stared at the stenotypist. They always fascinate me. They record every word said. In every courtroom, at every government hearing, everywhere in the land, there is a record of every word said. This is extraordinary. An absolute word-for-word record of every word said in all of the hearing rooms in the land.

At one o'clock the judge stood up and adjourned the court for lunch. The stenotypist shut down her machine. Until the court met again at 2:30, whatever words were said would be lost, except for the occasional word that haunts us for life.

On the steps leading down to Foley Square, West said,

"I don't feel like sitting in a Chinese restaurant on Mott Street. Is it all right with you if we grab a couple of frankfurters off that street cart?"

We ate two frankfurters on the corner of Worth Street and then started walking south toward the Brooklyn Bridge. On the top of the Municipal Building we could see an angel of justice. The Federal Building was a golden triangle. The Woolworth Building emerged to the west.

When we came to the Brooklyn Bridge, which is the only monument New York ever built, West stared at the bridge. It stood there linking Manhattan to Brooklyn as most men yearn to be linked to God.

"Do you think Emerson will sit in a courtroom with a stupid judge and a bored jury," West asked me, "no more able to explain himself to the court than the court can explain itself to him?"

"I don't see a courtroom as his confrontation," I said. "A Scopes trial. The black man pleading the case that he is actually human and all the things we have been saying about him are only bad history and bad manners.

A police siren interrupted us. Two patrol cars with flashing lights stopped at the entrance to the Brooklyn Bridge. The policemen got out of the squad cars and started pointing upward toward the cables. High on the bridge we saw a man standing upright, his body suddenly visible, more visible than the entire bridge.

"You see?" West said. "That man up there wants a confrontation! It must be a dazzling moment for him, but no more than a dazzling moment. Just as the act of murder is dazzling. But nothing is less dazzling than a corpse unless it is a corpse that we want to bring back to life again. This is what Emerson wants, to bring a corpse back to life."

"Do you actually believe Emerson is going to murder," I asked West, "to get his corpse?"

"Don't you?" he said.

"Not from what I have seen."

"Then you have to see more," West said. "What do you think that man up there on the bridge sees as he looks out on this city, with the police now crawling up toward his sanctuary? Whatever it is, the police won't see it as they climb toward him. If that man up there retains his vision, he'll jump. If he doesn't, the police will cart him off to Bellevue Hospital. He'll come down looking like a man who has nowhere else to go except where the police will lead him. This, you may have guessed, is the way I see Emerson. He's on a height."

"And why does this involve murder?" I asked West.

"Because this is the way most men die," West said.

We couldn't wait to see if the police reached the man high up on the bridge. I left West on the gray slab steps of Foley Square. He went up the steps to continue his defense of Robert Sims, who had murdered the grocer on East 98th Street, a stupid, useless murder, West told me, as most murders are, for we still cannot murder the fears that haunt us the most.

114

O N AUGUST 19 I traded Jenny Beal a couple of hours on New York's West Side for whatever she could tell me about Emerson.

Jenny Beal had a marvelous habit. When you gave her a light for her cigarette, she would take your hand, cup it, bring your hand up to her cigarette, hold your hand until the cigarette was lit and then return your hand to you in a way so natural that you thought this was what all Southern women did in families with an income of over $25,000 a year.

We left the cafeteria on 96th Street and Broadway for a walking tour. Jenny wore a cool black sleeveless dress and flat shoes. She carried a black alligator purse that was expensive enough to look like plastic.

"What's the first stop?" Jenny asked. "If you don't mind my saying it, all of this city looks like hell on an August morning when the humidity is over ninety. I can't believe any sensible people live here. They must have secret reasons for living in these buildings plastered up against one another. Washington, D.C., has buildings plastered up against one another, but they don't look like this. They have little parks in Washington, you don't get the feeling that the people have been sentenced to death." We were turning down West 99th Street toward West End Avenue, where the sentence of death had been passed.

I led Jenny up West End Avenue to a building I had studied for the Foundation, a building that looked like the Rock of Gibraltar from the outside. Two great wrought-iron doors led into a marble lobby. The lobby was chopped in half by a partition of chicken wire that separated the management from the tenants. I didn't see Harris, the landlord, behind the chicken wire.

Jenny and I crossed the lobby and entered an empty elevator. The buttons for the first, second, fourth, fifth and sixth floors were ripped out. I pressed number 7. The doors closed slowly, Harris had adjusted the doors after they had crushed the head of a six-year-old Negro girl. She slipped on garbage as she entered the elevator and the doors snapped shut on her skull, pushing her eyes out of her head and spilling her teeth on the elevator floor. In a moment of compassion after the accident, Harris told me, "She's better off dead. Automatically better off. Automatically there should be no more babies. The babies at Metropolitan Hospital shouldn't be born. The doctors should spend their days and nights killing the babies before they are born. I have three girls in this building right now who are under fifteen years of age who have bellies bigger than their mothers' and their bellies are full of living stuff almost as old as they are. Two girls from this building who were in the fifth grade had babies. The fifth grade! They do it on the roofs, on the stairs, in the elevators, in the toilets, in the hallways, in the rooms, in the parks. Two days ago I saw three punks come into the building, maybe fifteen years old apiece. I didn't recognize them, so I followed them up. They went into an empty toilet. I knew they went into the empty toilet to shoot dope into their systems. I kicked open the door and told them to get the hell out. The girl had a big belly filled with a baby. She had the needle in her arm when I kicked open the door. The needle dropped. She fell down on the toilet floor like an animal. She started licking up the stuff, licking it off that toilet floor. Get out, I screamed at them. Get out and kill yourselves." Eaton said one day that I should get Harris up to the Foundation for a lunch.

On the seventh floor, the elevator doors opened on a gray wall that used to frame a mirror for the tenants who had fled in the 1950's. The mirror had been shattered on the wall. In its place was the scribbling of children and again the curse words. A nameless prophet had wandered through the hallway writing on the walls: A BLACK NIGGER WITH NO EDUCATION IS A DEAD BLACK NIGGER! NIGGER LEARN TO READ AND WRITE! NIGGER READ THE BIBLE! READ THE CONSTITUTION! READ THE CIVIL RIGHTS ACT! READ YOUR OWN GOD DAMN IGNORANT MINDS!

Each apartment on the floor had been chopped into eight rooms, each room separated by plasterboard, with one toilet in the hallway for each eight families. The babies slept three in a bed, piled into double beds, bunk beds, cots, mattresses thrown on the floor—if there was room for a mattress, for the rats needed room to run into their holes. Over half of the families in the United States with five or more babies have incomes of less than $3,000 a year.

I knocked on room 7E3. Mrs. Evans came to the door. She was twenty-seven years old. She had four babies by four different men. When she came to the door I saw that she was pregnant again. She saw me glance at her stomach.

"It just happens, Mr. Brooks," she said.

"Can we come in?" I asked her.

"Sure. Let me put a light on." Mrs. Evans switched on a lamp. Her four babies were in bed. They were naked. They looked dead. Roaches crawled over them. Roaches crawled over the walls, on the tables.

Mrs. Evans glanced at the roaches. "Nothing keeps them out," she said. "Harris has a sprayer but nothing keeps them out."

"This is Miss Beal, a friend of mine, Mrs. Evans."

"How are you?" Mrs. Evans said.

"I'm fine, thank you," Jenny said.

"You're not from Alabama?" Mrs. Evans said.

"Yes," Jenny said.

"I keep thinking of going back. I still have an aunt there. It was better than this, but this can be better than that. You know what I mean?"

"Yes," Jenny said.

"I thought you were getting the hell out of here," I said to Mrs. Evans.

"I keep looking. But every place is worse than this, at least for four children. I wouldn't live in Harlem. I won't live in a lot of neighborhoods in New York. I went up to Brooklyn and I won't be back there again. This isn't so bad, except for the size of the room. There's the park outside on Riverside Drive and this is a nice street, even the junkies try to keep it a little neat."

"But you have no room here," Jenny said.

"Don't I know it," Mrs. Evans said. "I look for places and everything I see is worse. Harris hired a couple of private police and they patrol the floors at night. They keep a lookout for the junkies trying to make trouble and the muggers. You don't have too many break-ins like you used to. You couldn't leave anything in your room at one time. Everything would be stolen. Old clothes, radios, TV sets, knives, forks, baby clothes, food. I even had my baby's milk bottles taken. Now the private police keep that kind of stealing down. Nobody kicks in your door now with a knife ready to slash at you for what you've got. I know about the Harlem rooms where you have to put a chest of drawers up against your door at night so you can get some sleep. Where the junkies just rob and steal from old people, the sick, anybody. You said a change was coming over this city, Mr. Brooks. When do we see it? Will we have to crawl out of our graves to see it?"

The babies woke up and stared at us. They knew me, but they stared at Jenny as though the TV set were still going.

"Hello," Jenny said to them. Jenny didn't look at the cockroaches when she sat down on the bed to pick up the youngest child.

"Say hello," Mrs. Evans said.

"Hello," they answered Jenny.

"How old is the oldest?" Jenny asked.

"Seven, that's Judith."

"Is she in school?"

"Of course," Mrs. Evans said.

"Can she read?" Jenny asked.

"She better," Mrs. Evans said.

"Can I send her some books?" Jenny asked.

"Sure. We buy them at the Goodwill store on 124th Street for a nickel apiece."

"What are you going to do with this baby when it comes?" I asked Mrs. Evans.

"Do you have any babies?" Mrs. Evans asked Jenny.

"No," Jenny said, "no."

"How come?" Mrs. Evans asked. "You look like you could take good care of a baby. You're getting old not to have a baby."

"I'll have a baby," Jenny said, almost stiffly. Jenny was in her late thirties, the age of the swift descent when we can no longer pretend that life isn't everything we know it is.

"I've got four and one coming. I keep thinking about my four babies, Mr. Brooks. What if one of them grows up to be a United States Senator, one grows up to fly a spaceship somewhere, one grows up to be a doctor and one grows up to be a judge? This is the only property I've got in the world, Mr. Brooks. The only thing I own, unless somebody tries to take my babies from me. I don't own a single other thing except the junk you see laying around this room."

"But how can they grow up in a room like this?" Jenny asked.

"They weren't always in this room. I stay in this room now because of the school on 105th Street. That school has something going for it. Nobody at that school is afraid of black children. Am I dreaming, Mr. Brooks?"

"If they can read and write, if they know what's inside of books, if they don't stop learning and keep growing with the world and if you don't leave them, it's no dream. But what about the men who gave you the babies? You never include them in."

"They're gone, they go, you know that. They can't support me. None of them men makes as much as the checks I get downtown from welfare. They can't support me, those men. But the almighty United States can support me. I'm on their payroll. I'm working for the United States government, that's the way I see these welfare checks now. I'm employed, Mr. Brooks, I'm working. I get paid twice a month, just like other government workers. I get medical benefits, a pension, everything but a raise and a vacation. But it's a job. It's the best job I ever had, and I never had a job with such steady pay. And if I have ten more babies, that's ten more chances that one of them is going to make it."

Mrs. Evans' babies got out of the double bed. It was hard to tell from their faces if they had already been systematically and invisibly destroyed. The experts in Washington on environmental retardation said that children exposed to a slum environment, an environment without stimulation, love, warmth, available parents, books, ideas, language, spoken words, were systematically and invisibly destroyed just as though their brains were eaten away by syphilis. The destruction was invisible. It didn't show up in the children until they were forced to use their minds in the third and fourth grades of school. These grades forced them to use their accumulated knowledge, if they had accumulated any knowledge. In the fifth grade the children unable to conceive of themselves as a link to the world, unable to use their minds to link ideas, to form ideas, unable to think of themselves as important—these children began to fall back, the teachers compounding their failures, and by the end of the fifth grade these children were shattered, superfluous, without a link to the world they inhabited. They had no place to spring except to dependency, a dependency that took the form of drugs, retardation, schizophrenia, prostitution, crime, murder.

In the hallway Jenny said, "That woman, that room. Does she believe all the things she said about her children?"

"It'll take a couple more years to find out. If her daughter gets grabbed in a hallway toilet and some drunk gets her pregnant and there's no provision for an abortion, that's the end of her life."

I knocked on 7E10. Edith King didn't answer. I knocked on 8F4. Rene Roberts didn't answer.

"We don't have to invade any more privacy," Jenny said. "Let's just walk down these halls and down these stairs. That will be enough for me, because I'll never forget the smells."

I led Jenny into the community kitchen on the seventh floor. The kitchen had a stove with four burners, a wall of cupboards locked with padlocks, a refrigerator locked with a padlock, and inside the refrigerator there were individual cubicles with padlocks. This was a kitchen for eight families, Mrs. Evans included. The padlocks were needed because the addicts broke into the cupboards, searching for food. Jenny looked into the toilet for eight families. The tub was cracked, the shower was dripping and broken. The toilet seat was ripped off, the inside of the toilet bowl was splattered and stuffed with newspapers.

When we reached the ground floor, the cold marble floor, the cold walls of marble, the chicken-wire partition, when we saw Mr. Harris sitting inside of the partition writing out a rent receipt, when some of the sunlight forced its way into the lobby, Jenny said, "Maybe I ought to get a room here for a week or a month or a year. Maybe I ought to sit on those toilet seats. Cook in that kitchen. Sleep in those beds with the roaches crawling over me. Just the way the people from the North go down to the South to stay in a black man's cabin, live in the black part of town, eat in the black restaurants, sit in the back of the buses. I don't know what they accomplish. But I think I should try it."

"You couldn't," I said. "You would get murdered. I knew a girl from Vassar who moved into a building like this on West 104th Street. She moved into a building where she didn't belong, didn't fit and that she didn't understand. She used the hallway toilet. She used the community kitchen. She came out of the hallway toilet after taking a bath, wrapped in a towel. A junkie on the third floor saw her coming out. He figured she was a nut with money. He knocked on her door and when she opened the door he ripped off her towel, raped her, strangled her and took the twenty dollars she had in her purse, all in about fifteen minutes. The girl was dead forever and he was picked up in a bar on West 87th Street, two hours after the killing, eating popcorn and drinking beer.

"I knew a crazy probation officer who moved into this building three years ago because he thought he could get a better insight into his work. Two addicts beat him to death after feeding him to fifteen men on the floor of the community kitchen on the ninth floor. One floor of this building is filled with homosexuals, one floor is taken over by lesbians, two floors are filled with addicts. This is why Harris hires private police to patrol his building, so that the lesbians, the prostitutes, the addicts, don't get out of line. Harris says they need a place to live as much as anyone else. The lesbians in this building would tear you apart before you ever got out of the community kitchen."

"Then how does someone like Mrs. Evans stay here? And all the other women with babies?"

"Mrs. Evans said it—she likes the park and she likes the school and it is a lot worse elsewhere. She's right."

Harris saw us in the lobby and called us over to his chicken-wire partition. He opened the door, secured with a padlock, and let us in.

"Well," Harris said, "I see I'm still on your books. I'm beginning to think that I'm part of the Museum of Natural History."

"Miss Beal wanted a tour. She said that in Alabama they do things more out in the open. New York is a closed city."

"It's so closed," Harris said, "that in 1960, before they passed the Single Room Occupancy Law, it was perfectly all right for me to have living here four hundred babies and nobody in the city, state or Washington complained out loud. They were happy for me to take the babies off their hands. There was a commissioner then who used to say, Would you like to see the babies sleeping in the street? When the mothers used to complain to me about the rats, the drunks, the broken toilets that couldn't stay repaired for ten minutes, the junkies, the whores, the food taken from the refrigerators, the screaming at night, the murders, the pimps who used to come to steal the checks, I used to tell the mothers, Take your babies and sleep on the sidewalk with your babies rather than in these stinking rooms. But not one of them ever did it. Not one of them dared, or cared enough to dare. Can you imagine what would have happened if five mothers, only five mothers with their twenty-five babies, would have stretched out to sleep on West End Avenue because they couldn't stand the rooms for which this insane city then was paying $110 a month? But not a single mother did it then, and they were all on welfare, and they had nothing to lose but one night's sleep. But they didn't do it. It turned me into a philosopher, Miss Beal. I think you have them in Alabama too."

"What happened to the babies who slept here during the 1950's?" Jenny Beal asked.

"That's a good question for Washington to answer. I followed some of their careers. Three of them committed murder, senseless murders, kicking old people to death. About fifty were sent away. Most of the little girls grew up to be great big girls with great big pregnant bellies full of goo and they got thrown out of grade school, junior high school and high school. They got thrown out of school and into welfare, where they're rotting like their mothers. I had one boy that I used to give a quarter to run out and buy me cigars. He was picked up by a detective for hustling, selling his fourteen-year-old ass to the homosexuals on Riverside Drive. The boy called me because I was the only person in the world whose telephone number he had. I got him a lawyer and he beat the charges. I gave him money to go to Cleveland, where he had an uncle. He got a job with a cousin of mine and now he's making a down payment on a house within three minutes of Shaker Heights."

"And the others who didn't have your telephone number?" Jenny asked.

"I know when I have to feel responsible, Miss Beal, don't try to push it on me. The others? They rot. They rot in school. They rot in jails. They rot on the street. They rot when the police beat their brains out. They rot when they look for a job and can't read the want ads or fill out an application. Miss Beal, right now in this lovely city there are a hundred thousand mostly black children between the ages of fourteen and eighteen who are looking for work, who will never find work and who are already dead inside. I see them all the time because I recognize their faces. I know what they look like on the inside, like a runaway cancer that even scares the doctors. If you want to start a parade, Miss Beal, I'll help you to lead it."

"Did you ever think of what should be done with the hundred thousand?" Jenny asked Harris.

"Yes, Miss Beal, I think about it a lot. I would give each one of them a bank account of three thousand dollars. I would give each one of them a job with a lifetime guarantee. I would make them permanent civil servants. I would train them to sweep out the stinking subways. To pick up paper from the street, to pick up the dog duty, as my nephew calls it, which is making this city sick. I would get them to wash windows. To help old people cross traffic, to help women with baby carriages up steps. To help lift up old people in their beds in nursing homes so that they don't sleep wet all night. To wash down hospital beds so that they don't stink for the next patient. They would be out on the street, like the police, only their job would be to do everything that is good. Do you know why I would do all this, Miss Beal? Because each one of them is a cold-blooded murderer, because each one of them will kill and kill and kill if nobody pays any real attention to them. And they will kill more and more—not occasionally, as they now kill. They have a right to kill, because life was taken from them. They're empty, Miss Beal, empty of life, empty of love, empty of anything to do in the morning. There is nothing inside them. Their insides have to be filled up, pumped full of jobs, money, of links, Miss Beal—this is the important word, of links, the links that keep you and my good friend here, John Brooks, doing what you do. Talk won't help these murderers. We live by money, then everything else follows. They know this, if they know nothing else. We have been buying off half the world with money. We gave life this way to the miserable Germans, the miserable Japanese, the Greeks, the Turks, almost all of Asia. They were all dead. They all got our money and they all came back to life. The hundred thousand here are a separate nation, Miss Beal, a separate nation of murderers and the murdered, and I think we should buy them off too."

"It sounds so practical," Jenny said.

"Miss Beal, you're a Southerner, you know how to handle human life as a commodity."

"What does that mean?" Jenny asked.

"It means, Miss Beal, when the time comes, the South will give up a little to retain everything. That is why the struggle is being prolonged. To make the little bit look important. Now if you will both excuse me, I have to go up to the sixth floor to see the damage the junkies did to the toilet bowl."

Harris padlocked his door. Jenny and I crossed the marble lobby and went back into West End Avenue. In the hot humid sun I could see that Jenny was trembling. Her face looked white, then ashen, as though she was going to vomit on the sidewalk. A cab slowed up, seeing us on the sidewalk. Jenny took my arm. She controlled her trembling by pressing her fingers into my arm. "Let's get into the cab," she said, "I can't walk." The cab stopped. "The Gotham," she said to the driver. In the cab she said to me, "It's true, so much is true."

AT 82ND STREET, Jenny asked the cab driver to pull over to the curb. Her face was still white. There was sweat on her forehead. Her hands were cold as I got her out of the cab. Jenny leaned over and vomited, heaving out of her mouth whatever she had carried with her out of Harris' building. The vomit splattered on the curb, coming out of her mouth in two racking bursts. She held her head down for a minute after the vomiting stopped and stared in astonishment at the vomit-splattered sidewalk. I gave her a handkerchief. She wiped her face and mouth and we got back into the cab.

"I'm sorry," Jenny said to the cab driver.

"It happens, lady, this heat could make anybody sick. Do you still want to go on to the Gotham?"

Jenny turned to me. "Could we just ride around these streets?" she asked me. "You know, these are the blocks where Emerson lived when he first came to New York."

"If you're all right."

"I'm all right. This had to happen. The smell of the urine and the cooking fats made me sick. I had to throw it up. I don't think I've thrown up in years. It must be terrible to watch a woman throw up."

130

"Are you sure you want to ride?"

"Yes. I don't want to go back to midtown New York. That would be too unreal. I have a ten-dollar bill here. Let's ride till the meter goes up to ten dollars." Jenny opened her purse and put a ten-dollar bill on the seat. I leaned over to the cab driver and said to him, "We want to ride up and down these streets, going from east to west as far as 110th Street, and then we'll cut into Harlem."

"If you see one street, you see them all," the driver said. "They all stink. Didn't you see the papers last week? They finally found out that one million people ran away from this crazy city. Everybody that could crawl made the move to Rockland County, Jersey, the Island. The hell with my ceiling rent! I'm going to move too."

The driver turned sharply into 82nd Street toward Central Park West, passing buildings that had decayed the way children decay when they are left to rot in hospital wards, children whose brains turn soft, whose smiles vanish. Jenny sat close to the window, trying to catch a breath of fresh air out of the heavy, humid, filthy air. We were at 84th Street, the famous street that had successfully withstood all the efforts of New York City to rescue it from its filth. West 84th Street became famous in the 1960's because riots broke out on the block. After the riots, the priests and the ministers cried out, See, we told you so, we told you there would be riots, people can't live this way without exploding! New York City sent in experts to try and learn who lived on West 84th Street. The can of worms opened and spilled out on West 84th Street, which was no different from the rest of the blocks on the West Side. Out came the babies with their doomed faces, out came the sick mothers clinging to their doomed babies, out came the drug addicts, the drunks, the men who lived off the street. New York City quickly tried to hide the can of worms. Buildings were ripped down, landlords fined, volleyball courts set up in the middle of the block; homemakers, social workers, welfare workers, public-health nurses, building inspectors, psychologists—the whole ragged army was called up to fight 84th Street. West 84th Street fought back, house by house, rotten room by rotten room. The sick mothers, the sick babies, the drunks, the sick, the old, the pimps, thieves, the psychopaths—none of them were willing to surrender their world of failure; they clung to their world of failure and they defeated the ragged army of specialists who underestimated them.

"I walked this block with Emerson," Jenny said. "But I didn't see anything. Just people, a lot of people, a lot of babies. I carried a bag of groceries so that I would look like I belonged to the neighborhood. I didn't wonder at the number of babies. All I saw were men hanging around with nothing to do and the women sitting by their windows."

Jenny sat back in the cab, the ashen color gone from her face.

"Have you seen enough?" I asked her.

"Can you see enough? Let's keep riding until this ten-dollar bill is gone. I've never done this in a cab. This is the luxury way. This way you feel you're sneaking up on things. We're moving slow, which makes everyone look at us with suspicion. When a person suspects you, then you can see his real face. Did you ever see Emerson stare at someone he suspected, someone he didn't trust? Suddenly his face gets taut, his skin becomes so stretched that you can almost hear him screaming with pain. Emerson can squeeze his entire body into his face, you can feel him pushing inward. What a minister he would have made if he hadn't left Yale. He was famous at the Yale Divinity School for crying out, Fuck the white god, fuck the white god, come out of hiding, God, come out of hiding behind the white god. Yale had some tolerance. He wasn't immediately expelled."

"Where did Emerson say that?"

"Not in any church. He didn't post it on the cathedral doors. He said it when he was drinking beer with some divinity students and ministers."

"He didn't get thrown out of the Yale Divinity School, did he?" I asked Jenny.

"No. The Yale Divinity School is like the civil service. Very few people are thrown out of the civil service. They are politely asked to resign. Emerson wasn't asked to leave, that I know. He left Yale because he wanted to leave. He left because of what he calls the white man's religion. Emerson hates white men."

"I haven't seen it yet."

"Then maybe he has some reason for hiding it from you. He hasn't hidden it from West. Ask West to show you the letters Emerson has sent him. I think you'll find them remarkable. I know the letters shook up West, and he's not easily shaken."

"Then why does West keep seeing Emerson?"

"West is fascinated by Emerson. Sometimes he tells me he thinks Emerson is going to commit a murder, a very special murder that will attract a lot of attention. Sometimes he thinks Emerson is going to be a victim and Emerson's death will attract a lot of attention because he'll die as a martyr. I have a lot of respect for West when he speaks about law. I've heard West speak a great deal about lawyers. He thinks lawyers are going to be the next important people in our civilization. The lawyers will take over from the priests, the generals, the economic men and the scientists. West thinks lawyers will be among the few people able to grasp the kind of civilization we're coming into. Emerson now is somehow central to his thinking. West sees Emerson as a murderer or a victim who will be able to make explicit to him a lot of ideas that are still half born."

"Did Emerson ever turn on you?" I asked Jenny.

"Yes,"she said.

"How?" I asked.

The cab turned into West 104th Street past the two ugly buildings where I had planned to take Jenny from West End Avenue, but that part of the tour was over. Jenny stared at me, not at the buildings. I saw the face of a woman who asks only that you give her consideration for being a woman.

"Do you know how I met Emerson? West took me to a play in the Village. I came into New York after Selma. The play was at the Judson Memorial Church. Some group was putting on an *avant-garde* play, a stupid play that I can't even recall. The church there likes to make religion comfortable to people who couldn't care less about religion. But the church does get crowds and there is always the hope that God will win out in the end. Just get them inside is probably the Protestant war cry of this century. During the intermission West went up to Emerson, who was standing alone in the church lobby and looking as though he enjoyed standing alone. West brought him over to me. We shook hands. I remember that his hand was very hard. Emerson wanted my attention. He wasn't cool, he wasn't asking for credentials. I was impressed when West told me that Emerson had been a divinity student. Somehow we expect miracles from men who decide to make a career of the church."

"Were you impressed with Emerson?"

"Yes, but not immediately with anything that he did or said."

The taxi turned into West 109th Street. Jenny pointed to a brownstone on 109th Street. "That building!" she said. "Emerson used to work there." I asked the driver to slow down, just to get the address.

"What kind of work did Emerson do here?"

"The whole building is owned by a woman named Mrs. Moore. She seemed to be in her late sixties. I saw her once. She looked as if she had settled in the ooze of the building. She collects boys, mostly between the ages of seventeen and twenty-two. She has fifteen rooms in her brownstone and the rooms are always filled with men who have nowhere else to stay. They eat and sleep there and she tries to find jobs for them and if necessary she helps them with clothes and transportation. Her husband died about thirty-five years ago and she uses the money from the estate to keep the house going."

"What was Emerson's job?"

"First you have to know that when Emerson came to New York from the Yale Divinity School he roamed the streets of New York, going from one neighborhood to another, to all kinds of jobs, sleeping with different friends, finding odd jobs, he mixed with all kinds of people from Lower East Side poets to the parties given by Protestant ministers who were raising money to send Negro boys to prep school. When Emerson and Mrs. Moore got together, Emerson was out of money, he didn't have a job, he didn't have a place to stay. Mrs. Moore started talking to Emerson on one of those ugly benches we saw this morning on Broadway. I think that's where she sits to recruit the men for her house. When she learned Emerson had been in a divinity school, she offered him a job counseling the younger boys in the brownstone. Emerson took up the offer. He stayed with Mrs. Moore for two months. Emerson told me the house was filled with broken, disturbed, sick, shattered boys and men and their only excitement out of life was the homosexual orgies. Emerson stayed in the house because it was so isolated, so fantastic, so completely lost in the city, so unknown, that the obscurity attracted Emerson. He left Mrs. Moore when S. T. West offered him the job of working in the storefront church on 112th Street. That was the beginning between West and Emerson. Before that they had just known each other from seeing each other at different

Protestant meetings in the city."

The taxi moved slowly down West 112th Street and there, facing us, was the Cathedral of St. John the Divine, the third-largest cathedral in the world. The cathedral rose up from Amsterdam Avenue, the most unlikely place in the world for the third-largest cathedral. St. John was built of massive gray stone, a remote cathedral, uncompleted, with naked scaffolding its symbol. It was stuck in the middle of a civilization that no longer had use for its silence, its great columns, which was probably the reason why St. John the Divine had an endless building program, to give an inner life to itself.

"Let's stop here!" Jenny said. She gave the driver the ten-dollar bill and he looked at us as though we both needed the church.

We approached the steps of St. John. We could see Morningside Park, where the divinity students were warned not to walk, during either the day or night. A divinity student from Michigan had been kicked to death in the park by fifteen boys.

The inside of St. John was cool and dark. Jenny went down the aisle. She said nothing as we entered the cathedral. Midway down the aisle, Jenny took a seat. The vast cathedral was empty except for a few elderly men who sat apart. I sat down next to Jenny.

"This is so wasted as a place of worship," Jenny said. "This great aisle, this somber space. The cathedral should be open for meetings, for great movements, men with something to say and the power to back up their words ought to meet here instead of sitting in their air-

conditioned offices. How long could the West Side filth
that you showed me survive if it was discussed under this
roof? I'm always foolish about religious places," Jenny
said. "That's why I hate to see Emerson wasting himself.
Why can't Emerson meet here with West instead of
those East Side restaurants? Why can't Emerson speak
openly to West in this cathedral instead of writing West
those tortured letters? Now I think you must get those
letters from West. I'm so sick of those closed-off portions
of our life, the stupid silences. I've been to enough demonstrations in the North and the South to know how
deep and stupid the silence is. We can't talk to one another any more. Now that I'm sitting in a cathedral, let
me be confessional. Let me talk." Jenny spoke in a soft
voice, almost a whisper, though I felt she wanted to
scream out what she was saying.

"After the party at West's, I went home with the
young addict. You saw me leave with him. I have a very
bad habit. West may have told you about it. I like to
wander around Harlem at night. I stop and talk to
people. I go into streets that are probably as dangerous
for a Negro woman as a white woman. So far I've never
been bothered. I know some whites have been killed in
Harlem and not for any reason except that they happened to be in Harlem when the killers came upon them.
Emerson has told me to stop walking in Harlem. He told
me about a schoolteacher he knew who got thrown off a
roof. But I feel that I have to feel as safe in Harlem as
any Negro would want to feel in Mississippi. There have
been deaths in both places. I've been in Harlem alone

until two and three in the morning talking to people, and they stand on the corner with me until a taxi comes to take me back to the other country. I knew a white English journalist from *The Observer* who wanted to live for a year with a Negro family in Harlem and write about his experiences. It's never been done, I don't think. I haven't made any great discoveries in Harlem except that the black man is capable of great intelligence when he's himself and this intelligence fails him when he comes into contact with white people.

"I liked the addict. I thought he spoke brilliantly at the party. I thought he was pushed by that crowd to say some remarkable things and I wanted to hear what else he had to say. I thought I wasn't taking any great chance going with him, because West knew him. But addicts are unpredictable. I didn't want to get my throat cut by an over-anxious addict. I went to his room near here on 105th Street, which I wanted to see. I wanted to see his furniture, the furnishings, the things on the wall, whether he had anything in his room that meant anything to him. His room wasn't like the rooms we saw today, ugly, dirty. His room was bare, impersonal. He asked me to sit on the bed for a minute and then he said he would be able to take care of me. I didn't know what he meant. Then he took a hypodermic needle out of a jar of instant coffee and injected heroin into his arm. He then turned to me and said it would cost me twenty dollars if I wanted to spend the night with him.

"He said he had to steal that much money in order to be able to buy the heroin he would need for the morning

and if he stayed with me he wouldn't be able to go out
and steal. He told me that he would have to steal about a
hundred dollars' worth of cameras, radios, coats, TV sets,
whatever he could lay his hands on, to get twenty dollars
in cash, and so I should consider that I was getting a
hundred-dollar man.

"For a long minute I was tempted to give him twenty
dollars. I had never known a woman who hired a man for
that purpose. But I told him that I didn't want to go to
bed with him, that I was interested in what he had said
at the party. I said I just wanted to talk. He said he
didn't want to go to bed with me, he didn't want to talk,
that he couldn't guarantee my safety in the building because there were junkies on every floor and if they had
seen me and decided to rape me they would kick in his
door and he couldn't stop them. He said it was still early
enough for me to leave. He said he would have to leave
in a few minutes to go out and steal the money that he
needed for heroin. I asked him how he could live from
day to day on such terms. He said he didn't invent the
terms. I asked him if he had ever gone for a cure. Like
Mark Twain, he said, it's easy to kick heroin, I've done it
a hundred times. The more he spoke, the more I was
tempted to give him the twenty dollars.

"Finally he said, What do you want to do? I said, All
right, the twenty dollars is yours. You better get undressed,
he said, I'll shove this bureau against the door in case
some of the junkies try to kick the door in. Have many
women given you money? I asked him. Not many, he
said, but I seem to know when to ask for it. You don't

think I wouldn't have gone to bed with you if you hadn't asked for the twenty dollars? I said. You might have, he said, but I still need the twenty dollars for the morning. He started to undress, casually, as though he was on the beach, and then he stood naked in front of me. I think you ought to see what you're buying, he said.

"I saw a thin male Negro about twenty-six years old with almost no hair on his body and needle marks on his arms and thighs. His penis was full but soft, lying against his thigh, almost as though it was ashamed to stand up."

Jenny said, "I wish I could have dreamed this. It's so much easier to explain dreams and they are so conveniently forgotten. I looked at the naked needle-marked body the way my great-grandfather must have looked at the young male Negroes in the slave market of Washington, D.C. I didn't want to buy him for twenty dollars. I didn't want him to enter me, symbolically or physically, or lie on top of me. I've outgrown that. I had come to his room to listen to him speak because he did speak brilliantly in West's house, even if none of those people were listening to him. I thought his room in Harlem would be a place where the nonsense about drug addiction could be explained. He spoke with such clarity at West's."

Jenny paused to stare at a minister who approached the altar, and then she said, "I didn't go to bed with him. But it wasn't that easy. When he stood facing me he didn't have an erection. But when I told him that I didn't want to go to bed with him he got a terrible erection. I said, I can change my mind. He said, An addict can't. I said I wasn't an addict. He said, You're a Southerner, you're a junkie on this white-black crap. I said, I'm not, I know what you're talking about and I'm not. He said, Then why did you get hung up in this room? I said, I came here because of what you said at the party, because you spoke as though all of the knowledge about drug addiction was caught up in your experience. He said, Every junkie has the same experience, that's why none of them can get cured. I said, Then what's going to happen? He said, We're going to live until we die, that's what my mother told me almost every day of my life until I busted out. He still had a terrible erection. He started to move toward me. I said, No, that isn't what I want. He said, Nobody ever asks me what *I* want. Then suddenly he sat down on the chair in the room and covered his erection with his shirt. He said, Don't talk to me any more, because I've got to go out and steal twenty dollars. Maybe you'd better leave me twenty dollars because I'm not so sure I can go out any more tonight to steal. He got up from the chair and pushed the chest of drawers away from the door. He dressed and said, I'll walk you down to the street because you'll never make it on your own down these steps. We started down the stairs. I heard moans and screams and the banging of furniture, and on the stairway two addicts blocked our way. I got cold and very frightened. The two addicts didn't speak. They just stared at me. We moved toward them. They opened a passageway for us. When we got to the sidewalk I saw the automobiles moving, the people sitting on the stoops, the Good Humor ice-cream man, the children still out at ten in the evening, and it looked like I sometimes feel when I get up in the night in my room at the Gotham feeling as though this city and this country are somewhere at the edge of the world. I gave the addict the twenty dollars. He said he was going back upstairs to sleep."

Jenny got up. A minister was kneeling in front of the altar. Three divinity students walked past us. More people had entered the cathedral. We went up the great aisle of St. John the Divine, past the great doors, into the startling sunlight of Amsterdam Avenue. I put Jenny into a taxi. She said to me, "Don't forget to call West and get him to show you those letters that Emerson has been sending to him. He'll let you see them. He has to share them, doesn't he?"

WEST DIDN'T HESITATE to let me see the letters. He seemed anxious to be relieved of them. He told me the letter on top was the first letter Emerson had written to him, and he would never answer it. He said I was free to do so, if I could.

Dear White-faced, White-lipped, White-eared, White-legged, White-ass, White-mouth, White-nose, White-speaking, All-embracing White-friend from the White-church of the White-God, possessor of the Word, possessor of all that creeps and crawls, possessor of the power of the Sun, possessor of all the World but not the Black Soul.

I write to you from the other side of the world using the opening language of the original settlers of this broad land, the Red Indians who came across the sea from the Orient to live among the buffaloes and the still wilderness, unbroken, until England could no longer guarantee the simple religious freedom of a handful of poor protesters who came and founded this land which you now possess as the Indians once possessed the forest and as my black people once possessed themselves. The Indians

144

you have buried. But the black man came after civilization began in the still forests and you cannot bury him so easily. His bones cannot be easily dumped and thrown away, as you slaughtered the buffalo and Indian. The sun rises every morning on more than 20,000,000 black people. Where could you hide all the bodies?

I write to you, White-friend, because you have extended treaty terms to me and you want me to think that you no longer hate me as the lamb hates its butcher. On Constitution Avenue in that great shining capital city of the land you now possess I read under a protective glass the treaties written by the Indian chieftains to the white Congress, the chieftains trying to find in words what was being settled by bullets and starvation. No treaty could save the Indians. They are gone. They live on reservations. They were slaughtered. And there was no mercy. As a child sitting in the Nigger Heaven of the movie palaces in Baltimore I saw Indians shot down by the white men, who didn't even have to aim their rifles at the Indians. The Indians turned over dead, always killed by a single bullet. Never wounded, never hurt, never in pain, never bleeding, but always immediately dead. I was frightened then as a child of the white man's rifles, for if they turned on me or my mother or my father, we would never be wounded, never hurt, but dead. I guessed what being dead meant when I was two years old. Negro babies don't learn faster than white babies. They just learn the wrong things faster. A man should not know about death until he is old enough to make death important. We die so that others can live. But only if we live before we die. Which doesn't happen to many black men. Can you imagine me, White-friend, sitting at the age of five in the Nigger Heaven of Baltimore (you know Nigger Heaven refers to the balcony reserved exclusively for black children) knowing then that there was something false in the death of the Indians falling from their ponies? I never saw an Indian buried. Every Saturday morning the Indians died and I died with them. When the white guns were shooting down the Indians I would crouch in my seat in Nigger Heaven and pray that the guns wouldn't be turned against all the little niggers sitting in Nigger Heaven, for if you tried to penetrate the white seats of red velour or the white toilets you could get your head smashed against the white tile walls of the white toilets. Did this ever happen to you, great White-friend from the great White-church, did this ever happen to you when you were five years old? What frightened you at the age of five?

You extended the palm of peace to me, great White-friend. You gave me a suit of clothes off your back. You took me into the white world of the church on Washington Square. You took me into the white world of the martini cocktail on East 48th Street, where everyone looked at me as though I belonged over the bar nailed to the wall with a bronze plaque reading: Given to the patrons of the Givicci Restaurant by S. T. West, one adult male Negro who entered these doors on August 17, 1964, the first of his race to do so through the front door. It was the first martini I ever drank and I still remember the frost on the glass and the frost on the waiter. Why did the waiter tremble with rage in front of me, spilling just enough of my martini to let me know that it was deliberate? What made him tremble? Was it the blackness of my skin which is really brown? Was it the knowledge that I had penetrated an impenetrable sanctuary and he wanted me to know that if I lived to be a million years old I would always be delivered a spilled martini?

One idea haunts me, great White-friend who gave me a $275 used hand-tailored black suit which fits me like a barrel over my head. The idea that haunts me, great White-friend, is that I am now twenty-seven years old, and how will I now live with the great white man? I do not believe there will ever be a commingling of the whites and the blacks in the United States. I do not believe that we will ever be able to speak freely to one another. We will always speak to one another like a husband who comes hot and fast from the bed of a whore to his wife who knows his smell and the smell of a whore. This we can't escape. This is the sentence of the black man in America. How will I live with you then, great White-friend? How will I live through my middle years, my old age and my death? I can take no guidance from my mother or father. My mother told me early enough, Don't push so hard that they hurt you, and my father, he didn't talk, he was too ashamed. In all the years that I lived with my father we never sat and talked as I had seen some sons talk with their fathers in the movies in Baltimore. If I had been a writer or wanted to be, I would write dialogues of a black son with his black father. What did I want to know from my father? Pa, why does your driver's license say your eyes are brown when they are gray?

Great White-friend, I know how easy it is to take root in the failure of your parents, which is what Christianity has done with Jesus and Mary. Great White-friend, I do not want to take root in your failures. That is why I am addressing you from the other side of the world. Let me list your failures, great White-friend, keeper of the land. First, you do not believe what you believe. This is obvious. Second, you have no belief that you do believe in. Third, you feel the world is an unreal place and the only way to get through it is to race through the dark woods. Fourth, you are willing to be a victim of all that you do not believe, and I am not willing to be your victim.

What then is our relation to one another, great White-friend, for we do have a relation. What is it to be? Is it to be black man–white man? Is it to be father-son? Is it to be a dialogue, with you and me continually asking questions that would stagger the belief of a saner civilization? Are we to spend insane afternoons on East 48th Street over oak tables with heavy linen napkins resting on our laps and you asking me about Martin Luther King, demonstrations, Federal legislation, the University of Chicago papers on Negroes, the need for birth control among ten-year-old Negro girls, the high crime rate of black juvenile delinquents and white adults, public housing—what are we to discuss in the artificial darkness of East 48th Street? I have such a longing to smash all of the soft white faces I see on East 48th Street.

148

Are we always to speak as debaters? What should be the proper relationship of a black man to a white man? I know a black lawyer who sat down to lunch with a white lawyer and the white lawyer innocently said to the black lawyer, I would like to eat some really good Southern fried chicken. The black lawyer never spoke to the white lawyer again after that remark though they both worked in the same Wall Street firm. Can you imagine the black lawyer in bed that night twisting over in his mind the remark of the white lawyer and hearing in the remark a refutation of all that he had learned and earned at Harvard so that finally what he had to say to himself in bed that night was that he was still a black man, that was the total, that was all he had achieved? I think this happens to every black man in America because there is no escape from it. Is there a single black-white friendship in America that goes beyond color? I know white men marry black women and black men marry white women but this is not the same as being friends.

Do you know why I wanted to become a minister of God? I thought that if I could speak as a minister I would be listened to as a minister and not as a black man. I swiftly learned that the words of a white minister would sound foolish in the mouth of a black minister. A black minister is not a minister but a minister of black people. He has to speak as a black man to survive. No other man of God in America is under such a sentence. It becomes easy to hate God under such circumstances. But it is foolish to hate God because of what men do. I left

149

the Yale Divinity School because the Yale Divinity School is the last place on earth to experience God. If I was to be denied the experience of God in a divinity school, I saw no reason for being there. It was not my occasional bursts of anger that got me out of the Yale Divinity School, it was my direct perception that God had to be found elsewhere. I can say such things to you because you take seriously such problems as the perception of God, the experience of God, even though you have convinced yourself that you no longer have to be convinced about such issues. But I deny you access to God. I think this is what holds us together.

You are a great and famous trial lawyer. You rise in a courtroom to confront the court with its responsibility. I know you believe in a justice that escapes the penal code. I would like you to defend me if I ever went so far as to do the most extraordinary thing, which is to deprive a man of his life. I have murdered a thousand white men a thousand times but I think I would bungle the act if I ever actually tried to kill a man. What prevents me is the selection of a victim. Like you, I believe in individual justice. I couldn't kill any white man. That would be foolish. And I cannot kill all white men.

How would you have us act together, great White-friend? I will not lay down the terms except that I am prepared to give you access to God if you are prepared to give me access to America.

How can I give you access to God? How can I not give you access to God? How can you give me access to America? Great White-man, great White-friend, great White trial lawyer, great White drinker of martinis, great White party-giver, great White-friend of the black man—you do not have America to give to me.

                                        Thomas Emerson

I WROTE A MEMO to myself and said: Get more letters from S. T. West.

This letter was hand-delivered by S. T. West's secretary.

Dear White Father That I Never Had:

The riots are in the papers. By this morning they have digested the riot for you. It's all clean, crisp, accurately observed, like a laboratory report on a cancer in the lungs. I was in the riot. I was in the middle of the riot. I was flung into the riot. I raced through the streets. I screamed and yelled and hurled bricks when I had them in my hand and I might have killed you if you had been in the streets.

I heard screaming at eleven a.m. I looked out of my window on West 117th Street. I saw crowds rushing into Lenox Avenue and up Lenox Avenue. I thought the time had come for the torch to be put to Harlem as the villagers in horror movies put the torch to the monsters. I must have seen five thousand people in the streets. It was a great solid black mass, a black river. I rushed out of my apartment onto Lenox Avenue to see where the black river was going. The thousands of people were rushing up Lenox Avenue to 125th Street. This wasn't the kind of riot the newspapers always report, the criminal gangs of children breaking into the liquor stores, TV stores, carrying out color TV sets. This was a solid river, a black mass. I joined the mass. Most of the people in the mass were from the public housing projects and they were rushing toward 125th Street to protest. What had happened? A child was raped in the project at Lenox Avenue and 115th Street. Near the raped baby was a dead little black boy. His penis had been cut off. There was a note on his body saying ONE BLACK PRICK LESS. It was the killing of a sick person but the news swept through the project and all of the projects that extend to the East River. All the beatings, robberies, all the violence of the housing police, all the white hate, all the fear and hate of one another, it all formed into the solid mass rushing toward 125th Street. Then there was the rush of police sirens. Then the police came. Then the police horses. Then the police cars and their whirling red lights. Then the loudspeakers. Suddenly there was a helicopter flying low on 125th Street as though it was going to machine-gun the crowds. The helicopter swooped in low directly over the heads of the people and they threw up their hands, trying to pull down the helicopter. I didn't believe my eyes. The blades of the helicopter stopped whirling. It plunged into the welfare building on 125th Street. There was a terrible burst of flames, then an explosion, then screams, then we could see the building on fire, the file cases going up in fire. The crowd rushed for the police cars. The police fired into the crowds. When their guns were empty of the six or seven bullets the crowds tore the police to pieces. Their arms were pulled off, their legs, their eyes pulled out. One black man went among the dead police cutting off their pricks. The mob had now grown to about ten thousand because all of 125th Street was packed with screaming people. All the streets leading into 125th Street were being sealed off by patrol cars. Fire engines sealed off 125th Street from the east and west. More helicopters appeared in the sky. A voice cried out from the helicopter, Go home, go home, no more killings, go home, go home. Then the mob turned like a fantastic dragon. It turned into Fifth Avenue, where the police with their machine guns didn't dare open fire. The mob went down Fifth Avenue. The helicopters tried to swoop down on the mob but they couldn't drive back the mob. One black man picked up a machine gun from a squad car and started firing at the helicopter overhead. It burst into flames, falling into the mob. But still the mob didn't stop. It swept down Fifth Avenue. I let myself be carried with the mob, screaming at the top of my voice but I didn't know what I was screaming. There were no police cars now in front of us. The avenue was clear. We swept down Fifth Avenue, nothing could stop us, we swept on toward St. Patrick's Cathedral, Saks Fifth Avenue, the University Club. Then the police appeared. At 86th Street they were waiting with machine guns. Rows of police with machine guns. Get back, get back, the black women cried to the men, get back. The black women began gathering up the black children, they forced their way into the front of the line. Black women and black children in the front. There must have been a thousand black women and black children going toward the machine guns. Then they linked their hands and started going right up to the machine guns. The machine guns opened fire. You know what happened next, Great White Father That I Never Had? I woke up. I couldn't sleep because what we had been talking about until two in the morning wouldn't let me sleep. You see how poorly I describe a dream.

What was the relation between my practical nightmare and what we were talking about? Is a dream a disguise? Is a dream the actual truth? Is a dream what we don't dare put into words? Is a dream the taste of life that we can have, if only we dare?

You asked me if I wanted to be a lawyer. You said that you could probably arrange for me to get into the Harvard Law School, where you graduated, or into Columbia, where you are a trustee, and if none of them would have me, NYU would. Maybe you're confused about the kind of law that interests me, Great White Father That I Never Had. I don't want you tampering with my life. I have had the Protestant tampering for ten years, ever since a committee told me that I could have the choice of three Eastern prep schools and that I could get an education denied to eight million black children. When New York had its Double Discovery, 160 black children were taught English, math, taken to see the statue at Rockefeller Center—160 black children, out of all the black children, were double discovery. This is a dream,

155

White Father.

My mother and my father when I went to Harvard knew no more about Harvard than they did about the foreign policy of Yugoslavia. At Harvard the white boys thought I was a faggot. That is a dream. The beautiful black girls are always viewed as whores. A white man cannot look at a beautiful black girl without thinking that she is a whore. At Harvard the white boys thought I was a faggot. I was tempted to let some of the white boys suck me, but that would have perpetuated the dream. I survived that. Do you know what I learned at Harvard? I learned a foreign language. I learned the English language.

Do you know, White Father That I Never Had, what I was like at six years of age, seven, nine, eleven, fifteen, do you try to guess or do you only see me as I am now, a black boy who went to Harvard and Yale, so that I need no further looking? In 1953 my family lived for nine months in Harlem. My father thought he could do better in Harlem than in Baltimore. That's a Negro delusion in America, thinking one can always do better somewhere else. Like all of the black people who come to New York, we stayed with relatives until we knew where we were at. My mother, good for her, was horrified and sick of Harlem. My father would tell her that Harlem wasn't all of New York, that New York wasn't a Southern state, that there were places in New York where the black people lived better than the white people and made more money than they. This was my father's one try at the new world as an immigrant. We lived on 126th Street, which

is now known as the pit of Harlem. It's a filthy rotten
street. We knew it from the first day. We also had relatives on West 144th Street. The first time I went to
144th Street I didn't believe my eyes. Take a taxi ride
there, White Father, and you will see that all of the
billion-dollar projects in America haven't touched the
filth of 144th Street. It is more rotten than anything I
have seen. I went one morning to see my relatives on
144th Street. When I got to the block a gang of black
boys stopped me. They circled me. They saw I was different. They could smell Baltimore on me or Chicago, not
New York, not 144th Street. I couldn't fight them.
There were ten of them. The leader of the gang, black, a
stinking empty face, said to me, Get off this block, don't
ever come back or we'll kill you. Period. I said my relatives lived on the block and I wanted to see them. The
leader said again that if I didn't go they would take
me up to the roof of the building he pointed to and
throw me off the roof. I said, did that mean that I could
never see my relatives? The gang leader said, It means
that you stay off this block, that you don't walk on this
block, that you never show your face here because if you
do I will kill you. I'm paraphrasing his speech. What he
meant to say was that he had selected a lonely spot of the
earth to be his and he would not give it up. I knew
enough from my days and nights in Baltimore to leave
the block without any further argument. But that night I
couldn't sleep. I had to come to New York with my family for a new world and now that world was already being
limited. I couldn't walk on 144th Street. What other

157

blocks couldn't I walk on? I multiplied the blocks in my mind, for the second day we were in New York we drove in my relatives' car through the crazy blocks of New York. I knew I couldn't fight the gang on 144th Street, they were as mad as soldiers in a war who try to take an insane hill that nobody wants.

I couldn't sleep. But I had to pretend sleep. In that stinking apartment on West 126th Street where nine of us slept, I had to pretend that I was asleep because if I tossed and turned, the others in my bed wouldn't be able to sleep. I knew my father had a gun. Almost all Southern men who can afford it own a gun. My father didn't know that guns were against the Northern law and he brought the gun with him. I wanted to see my relatives on West 144th Street and I didn't want to let a bunch of black idiots keep me off of a public street. I wanted my stupid freedom. I took my father's gun and stuck the gun in my pants. The gun had six fat bullets in it, as the Southern sheriffs like to say. I walked the next night to 144th Street. The gang immediately recognized me. The gang leader came forward. It was his right to claim the kill, to drag me up the five flights of a brownstone to the roof and fling me to my death. I waited until he was seven feet from me and I was with my back to a wall where nobody could jump me. I pulled out the gun. There it was in my hand with six fat bullets. I pointed this deadly thing at the gang leader. I had my finger on the gun trigger. I had his life in my hand—now I know what the phrase means. I knew how to shoot a gun. In the South a boy can shoot a gun even if he can't always shoot a man or a boy. I said to the gang leader, I want to see my relatives, if you don't let me, then I'll kill you. I had the gun pointed straight at his chest where I couldn't miss. The gang leader must have been fourteen or fifteen. He had a thick dumb face, but there was a flicker in his face, he really didn't want to die for a street that didn't belong to him in the first place and to which he would never have a claim. He gave himself a minute of studying the gun in my hand and he saw that my hand didn't shake. He saw that the gun was real and death was real. Which is more than I saw, for I don't believe I knew how real death could be then. If I shot him, he would get up and walk away, maybe in pain, but he would walk away, because nobody dies this way. But he had seen more dead bodies than me and he knew more about death than I'll ever know. He said, and again I'm paraphrasing, he said, You're from out of town, you're an exception, you can see your relatives, we don't have to fight this one. What he meant to say was, I want to live because it's the only thing I can do. That was one of the last violent acts of my life, White Father.

White Father That I Never Had, you just don't know my history.

Thomas Emerson

I NO LONGER READ the letters as though they were written only to S. T. West and I was reading over his shoulder. They were written to me, I couldn't escape them. Nor did I want to. I found myself wanting to know from Emerson what escaped me in history, my history, what had been withheld from me.

Dear White Man With No Ears:

I write to you because you have no ears. You cannot hear me. Whatever I say, you do not hear. I have studied your face as I speak to you. I see no indication on your face that you hear me. You are never listening to me, but listening for something. I am the something. But since you have no ears I cannot expect you to listen. But the typewritten word makes us equal because then you are looking at the ultimate mystery, language, the words we have given to ourselves to explain ourselves.

On Friday I went to your world, Foley Square, to the Criminal Courts building at 100 Centre Street. This is the most ugly building in the world. The father of one of the children who comes to the church, Charles Gordon, was arrested on West 119th Street for resisting arrest and attacking two police officers. Does that sound familiar to you?

This is what happened, White Man With No Ears. Charles Gordon is twenty-eight years old. His son who comes to the church is ten years old. His name is Robert. Robert likes to run the mimeographing machine, which means that one day he may become a minister. Charles Gordon works in a print shop. He is trying to save enough money to move away from West 119th Street. On Saturday morning Charles Gordon was washing his car. Two policemen rode up alongside him in a squad car and asked to see his driver's license. Gordon said, I'm just washing my car, what do you want with me? One of the police grabbed Gordon and shoved him up against the car. Get your license out and cut out the shit, the police officer said. Gordon said, I'm not talking shit, I'm just washing my car, I just finished breakfast and my wife and baby and boy are in the house and in about fifteen minutes we're going for a drive to the Bronx Zoo. The police officer said, You prick, you're not going anywhere! Gordon said, What did I do? I was just washing my car. The police officer didn't answer. He took Gordon's license, studied it and gave the license back to Gordon. Gordon then said, Can I go in now? The two police officers said, Get in the car, you're coming with us! What did I do! Gordon cried out. His loud voice irritated the police officers. They slammed him up against the squad car. One more fucking word out of you and we'll kick your teeth out, the two police officers said. Gordon got into the police car. The officers told him to lie down on the floor of the squad car and not to move. The police officers didn't speak to Gordon during the ride to the station house.

In the station house, Gordon said, What did I do? Gordon said, I want to call a lawyer, I have a right to call a lawyer. The two police officers said, Shut up, you black prick, shut your cocksucking mouth. Gordon walked over to the telephone on the desk and said, The law says that I have a right to telephone for a lawyer. One of the police officers pulled out his gun. He pointed the gun at Gordon and said, If you pick up that phone I'll blow your black fucking head off. Gordon didn't move. He didn't dare move. The two police officers moved toward him, they slammed him against a table and kicked him as he fell to the floor. They then arrested him for assaulting two police officers and resisting arrest.

I went to the Part 1A court, White Man With No Ears, to see how justice would greet Charles Gordon.

The Part 1A court, White Man With No Ears, which is your invention since nobody asked me my advice, is where the Yale Divinity School should set up its tabernacle. The Part 1A court is a black man's court, for there are no white men in the court except the police, the judge, the lawyers, and even the black people working for the court look white. The prisoners are almost all black. The Part 1A court, I quickly learned, is where all the crime that is committed in New York must be immediately judged. This I learned is known as arraignment.

I sat next to a white man in the court in the second row. I wore my $275 suit which you had given me. The white man immediately recognized my $275 suit because

he was also wearing a $275 suit. He said to me, This fuck-
ing judge is out of his mind. I smiled. He continued. He
said, Not only is this fucking judge out of his mind but
this fucking court is out of its mind and the whole place
ought to be leveled to the ground. I smiled. He continued. He said, I've got to hang around this court because
some white pig accused my client of rape. One look at
the pig would tell you that she couldn't be raped. But my
client is black and the pig is white. He was driving home
from work, the nut, when he stopped for a red light in
Chelsea. This pig opened the door to his car. That
should have been a cue for him to slam the door shut and
take off against the light. But the pig was white, young,
looked attractive, at least in the time that he had to see
her while the light was changing, and she said it would
only cost him twenty dollars. He said, Move in. When
she got into the car they looked for a place where she
could go to work. He didn't want to take her to his apartment, for a very good reason—he lives in a middle-
income project with his wife and three children. Finally
he said to her, Maybe we'd better call this thing off. He
made the mistake of not giving her the twenty dollars or
at least a five-dollar bill. The pig called the police, gave
them a solid description of my man and the car and said
she had been raped. He has no defense unless the yellow
sheet proves the pig is a whore. I smiled at the white
lawyer and couldn't understand why he was telling me, a
complete stranger, the details of his case, unless it was his
way of telling me that the Part 1A court didn't exist,
wasn't real and he had to confide in me to keep his sanity

as he waited for the case to come up.

Everywhere in the court, White Man With No Ears, I saw only black prisoners. They were the criminals. Every time the door opened to the bull pen with its wire cage I saw a black man come up to stand before the judge. Tell me, is all the crime in New York committed by black people or do the police only catch the black men who commit the white crimes? If a prisoner said he could not afford a lawyer for the defense of his liberty, and almost none of them could, a Legal Aid lawyer stepped forward and within seconds—yes, seconds—this lawyer would make a decision that would affect the future life of the black man he was defending. It is a dazzling assignment that these Legal Aid lawyers have, but it is not justice. Justice, as you know, White Man With No Ears, means having enough money to pay for your own defense.

Hour after hour I watched the heads roll as they emerged from the bull pen. Now and then I would see a white face. But the black faces never ended. You cannot escape history, White Man With No Ears, as you sit in this court. Because the history of each black man is announced to you as he appears before the judge. This is the history you hear. The black men who appear before the judge have no jobs, no skills, no family, no income, no immediate relatives, no fixed residence, they are the superfluous men. Yet here they were in a temple of justice. Brought in from the isolation and anonymity of the streets. Bound over to the law. And the law was useless in front of them.

I stayed in the court until it closed at five. Charles

Gordon didn't appear before the judge. The two policemen who arrested him were ill. The case was put off for
another day. How can Charles Gordon defend himself?
He has already been beaten by being forced to appear in
court to prove his innocence of a guilt that never existed.
He can never forget this. Neither can the black men who
come out of the bull pen hour after hour, even though
they may be technically more guilty than Charles Gordon. How many more obscure inquisitional institutions
are there in this great Northern city? I know why you
seek out the black man. But why can't you find him?

Come and find me, White Man With No Ears. I am
not so far away. Come up to the storefront church and
listen to what the children include in their prayers. Yes,
and read the book you wrote about the Protestant God,
read what you wrote about God. How you wrote that
nothing is more obscure than a God we don't want to
see. And reread that article you wrote for *Commonworld*
which you modestly told me brought you 300 pieces of
mail, the article so permanently cast into black and
white. Black is the color we read. What did you finally
say in your article?

Do you know what you wrote? Do you know what
guided your hand? Do you know, White Man With No
Ears, that we are approaching a new madness where people no longer believe what they see written because they
no longer know who to believe? This is what you wrote,
pig, motherfucker, fatherfucker, cuntsucker, selffucker,
motherfuckingnogoodsonofabitch. Do you see how harm-
less the curses are, how they fall into senseless wasted

words? For why should fucking be a curse unless we think of existence as a curse?

This is what you wrote and I address you without a curse because I know that we both have eternity to face. In your article you said we (meaning everyone but the black man) should love the black man because God made all of us. You wrote that. You felt it necessary to establish in the year 1966 the extraordinary truth that the black man is created as a result of the same acts as a white man. Then you wrote that there is no evidence that the black man has a lower IQ than the white man, etcetcetcetcetcetc. Then you wrote that the history of religion is a history of returning to first beliefs, a refining of these beliefs, just as gold is never weakened by refining. Then you went on to say that your original religion never excluded blacks and it was now necessary for all the Protestant bodies to accept the blacks because a religion can never be hurt by returning to its first ideas. You wrote that if religion is to have a meaning it must have a meaning within the actual practice of the religion, for there is nothing exterior to a religious belief. You ended your article by writing that the Protestant religion was the most natural religion ever conceived by man with the help of God.

You know I believe in God. You know that I know that you believe in God. It is this belief that holds us together. Nothing else. For on no other level do we think the same. Now what is this God we both believe in? How shall we identify him? How shall we make him speak? How shall we listen to him? Do we both mean the same thing when we say we believe in God? Does our believing in God make any difference to God?

This is what I mean when I say I believe in God. I am frightened. I am frightened of the open spaces of the sky. I am frightened of the open spaces of my mind. I am frightened by the haphazard way we are born and the haphazard way we die. I am frightened by death and the instant of death. But so is life instant. In the neighborhood of the church I see a lot of epileptic children and asthmatic children, both of whom choke for life. What else is the trembling of an epileptic child when he has to throw himself on the ground and out of his mouth comes a white churning substance? Do you know that most of the children in the church are asthmatic? Do you know that their asthmatic choking is an expression of their wish to die? There is a plague of these children in Harlem. The asthmatic children are the children of God. In the black pits of Harlem they are the sweetest, most charming, most sweet, most intelligent of all the children in Harlem. And when they begin to lose their breath, to choke, to gasp, they are begging God to release them. But at the same time they are willing to suffer so that they can live. Asthma is what I call a God disease. Epilepsy is a God disease. Since neither you nor I have asthma or epilepsy, what then is our God disease?

I think I know your disease. You are part of the privileged white class in America, the very privileged, whose passage through life is as smooth as a Cook's tour. You don't want to make any mistakes. You are aware of your advantages, and your disadvantages haunt you. For whatever is rotten in American life is rotten because you permit it to be so. There is no other group in America, White Man With No Ears, like you, W.A.S.P., which is a greater title than all the grand titles of Europe, for you control all of the power there is to control. Your disease, then, is that you are rotting. There is rot in your bones. There is rot in your God. Your churches have rotted away. There is a not a preacher to halt the rot. You know the power you control and you know your powerlessness to use this power. Isn't this a disease of God?

I have the black disease. The black disease is this. I have to expend from 20 percent to 30 percent of my energy, my physical, intellectual, social energy, on the imprecations of color. This means that I am forever less than what I am. This is what a disease does to the body. That is why I believe in God. Because when we deal with God there are no imprecations. Most of the men I meet even under the best of conditions can only see a part of me. There must be a way for them to see the greater part of me. God never sees only a part of the truth.

How do I know God exists? How could he not exist? Throughout their history the Hebrews never gave up a part of themselves. This has been their extraordinary triumph. This is why the Jewish people are hated by the black people of Harlem. The Jewish people have always lived in the world of men. This is another reason why the black people hate them. Today the black man is more isolated than he has ever been. This is the black disease. Isolation. He is isolated from himself, his family, his chil-

dren, his work, his home, his dreams. Because of this isolation some black men abandon their families, most
abandon their children. But all abandon a part of themselves. This is the black disease that destroys the black
children. I write to you, White Man, because you have
no ears.

Thomas Emerson

DEAR W.A.S.P.:

On a Monday I went to the Port Authority Bus Terminal on West 40th Street and I bought a bus ticket for Cleveland, Ohio. I sat back comfortably in the bus and rode directly into the riots going on in Cleveland.

I had never participated in a riot, and like those pilots who enter the eye of a hurricane, I wanted to see what it would be like to enter the eye of a race riot.

I got off at the bus terminal in Cleveland, Ohio. I know Cleveland and I took a taxi directly to the riot area on Hough Avenue. I saw clusters of black people on the sidewalk. I joined the clusters. As they ran, I ran. When they shouted, I shouted. When they hurled bricks, I hurled bricks. The Cleveland police charged us and I ran to escape the police because I didn't want to be removed from the scene of the riot. I retreated with a cluster of blacks to a side street and in the dark I listened to what they were saying in the cluster, a black cluster that you could not have entered with a cross of gold.

One Cleveland boy, bleeding, tall, thin, his face cut, his face alive for the first time in seventeen years, this boy cried out, "Let's get one white pig! Let's strip his fucking white skin from his body and mail the white fucking skin to the President of the United States!" One quiet black man about forty-five took out a pistol. It was a German Luger. He held the pistol in the flat of his hand and said, "I found this thing when we entered Berlin. The city was on fire and we were shooting every German that moved, we were shooting down Germans like ducks and wherever they ran we chased them and we shot them and none of them could scream and get away, we just shot every German until their bodies began to pile up in the street and all the time the city was on fire, burning to the ground. That's what we should do to this fucking city, burn it to the ground and kill and kill and burn until we've burned out the plague in this city. Who's going with me to start a plague? We'll go into Mt. Sinai Hospital and kill every fucking first newborn white baby in the white cribs!" No one answered him. He slipped away, the pistol in his waistband, and none of us knew if he was going off to Mt. Sinai Hospital to kill all the newborn babies in their cribs. Should I have stopped him? Would you have stopped him?

Then the Cleveland police brought out a big searchlight. The searchlight sent a beam up into the black sky. Then the beam lowered on the blacks in the clusters. The searchlight was a mistake. Get the beam! Get the beam! became the cry. You can understand the cheap symbolism. A black boy of fifteen cried out, "I'll get the fucking thing! I'll get it!" He held a Pepsi-Cola bottle filled with gasoline. A black voice, an older black voice, said to the boy, "Don't you be a nut. They'll shoot you down in the street." "They won't even know I threw it!" the boy cried out. The older man grabbed the boy and said, "Put that bottle away. That beam don't mean anything. It don't mean enough for you to get killed!" The boy said, "They can't shine that thing on us! We didn't do anything! They did all the doing! I'm going to get that fucking thing!" "You'll get killed!" the older man said. "Fuck getting killed!" the boy said. The older man grabbed the boy and said, "I said you're not going to give them a chance to kill you! Live, boy, don't let them kill you. This ain't the real fight. This is just to scare us! They're scared. This whole city is scared. They got all the guns out and they're still scared because they figure we've got nothing to lose by dying and they've got everything to lose by dying."

Just then the searchlight blew up. There was smoke and fire by the searchlight. The police began shooting up into the air. Then thousands of blacks started yelling and running. The automobiles became the target. That shining object that gives the black man mobility to travel in circles. The automobiles began exploding, cars went up in fire, the mob of blacks sacrificed the cars in a rite as old as fire. The police kept shooting up into the air but the bullets didn't frighten anyone. The police would have never dared to fire directly into the crowd, not as the British did at Lexington. Because then the black revolution would have started in Cleveland. Then the lantern would have flashed the word to the blacks that the war was on that Alexis de Tocqueville envisioned.

Now I come to the afternoon of your party. That same afternoon Roger Holmes, who is fourteen and who occasionally comes to the church, was picked up on a roof on 114th Street for using heroin. His sister, age eleven, gave birth to a baby that same morning at Metropolitan Hospital. Just before I left the church, I received two phone calls. One phone call informed me that the eleven-year-old Esther Brown, who gave birth to a baby, was impregnated by her older brother who was now in Rockland State Hospital. The other phone call came from Mrs. Rector, who told me that her thirteen-year-old granddaughter, Roberta, who comes regularly to the church, was pregnant and what should she do? Mrs. Rector reads the Bible to her four grandchildren every night. She has been getting money from the New York City Department of Public Welfare to raise her daughter's four children. Her daughter is in Pilgrim State Hospital.

I walked from the church to West 93rd Street. I walked from where Harlem ends at 110th Street to where it begins again now at 109th Street, for the old boundaries of Harlem have split and Harlem is now all of America. I could see glimpses of the Hudson River and New Jersey beyond. I could see great expanses of the sky. Why, I thought, can't all the children of Harlem be shipped to where there is a great expanse of sky? But there is a great expanse of sky in the South! Did you know that we used to ship children from the slums of New York to the Middle West farms and we stopped the shipment of children when there was no more use for the labor of children on the farms? When I say *we*, excuse me for meaning America.

What will happen to the one-day-old baby of Esther Brown? Tell me, Mr. W.A.S.P., could your government, America, raise the baby delivered by eleven-year-old Esther Brown so that the baby will automatically have the advantages that are the standard operating equipment of a one-day-old W.A.S.P. baby? Do you know what I learned at Harvard? That the Federal government is now involved in a master longitudinal study of 50,000 babies for a fifteen-year period. The first reports of this master longitudinal study of 50,000 babies indicates that babies need good pre-natal care, good post-natal care, good food, a good mother, a good father, a good home and an income that never ends. What does a one-day-old baby delivered by an eleven-year-old mother who sat through the fourth grade in a New York public school without her teachers knowing she was pregnant, what does this baby need—a master longitudinal study?

I walked from Harlem to West 93rd Street, into your building, past the doorman with a .38 pistol under his left arm, and when I entered your living room with most of the people assembled, I realized the one-day-old baby could be dumped into a garbage can or ground up for dog meat.

Why did you give the party? For Jenny Beal? She hates New York cocktail parties. Then I met your friend again, John Brooks. He came to the door looking like a CIA agent. He shook my hand as though he was taking my blood count. Why?

John Brooks has an important reputation and after the

first shock of the way he stared at me, I tried to relax with him. I think he wrote a brilliant book. I know he has a reputation for telling off every phony in the social-welfare business and being able to deliver a hatchet blow to them if he feels they are dangerously stupid, which most of them are. But I didn't feel dangerous or stupid. I tried to relax with Brooks but he couldn't relax with me.

What could you have said to John Brooks about Thomas Emerson? This is the question I've been asking myself. These are some of the answers I've given myself.

You invited John Brooks to the party to meet me to see if I was fit to run a storefront church. You thought it was time I should meet John Brooks again because of my comments on some of the things he has done. You thought the storefront church was one of the best ideas to come out of the Protestant pot and you wanted John Brooks and me to get into a corner and talk about the new church. You wanted to find out if John Brooks could see in me what I've been putting into the letters I've been sending to you without his knowing anything about the letters and if so, would I be dangerous to the Protestant pot. Maybe you already showed the letters to John Brooks. He would be about the only person you would trust to see the letters and you wanted Brooks to decide what the letters really meant. Maybe you thought John Brooks would be an interesting victim for me.

I have just picked up the New York Times in my room to read the headlines as though they are relevant to me. I've gone to the refrigerator and I've dialed the telephone. In a word, I've done a number of things to reas-

sure myself that I am nothing more or less than Thomas
Emerson, because this is what I really think: I think you
made that last speech at the party directly to me and that
all you can see in me is a stupid act of murder.

This is just like you W.A.S.P., to always look for a victim. This is why America is a nightmare now. You saved
your speech about murder until Jenny Beal, John Brooks,
you and I were in the kitchen, and though you drank a
lot of bourbon you were sober. You spoke as you do in
the courtroom, in absolute control of the English language, so that no one, not even the most stupid juror, can
mistake the intent of your speech. Do you think I will
murder you? Do you think I will be murdered? Do you
think we are engaged in a murder together? If I murdered you, what would I be murdering? If you murdered
me, what would be murdered?

Thomas Emerson

ON AUGUST 29, Emerson telephoned me and by the sound of his voice I knew he was inviting me into his world.

"I'm having trouble up here," Emerson said, "that I'd like to talk to you about. Are you free today?"

"I can come up within an hour."

"Good. Come right into the church. You'll see something interesting then."

When I walked into Emerson's church the monsters were singing. Emerson stood on the altar leading the singing. He wore a gray sweat shirt and khaki pants. Above Emerson I could see the dazzling wooden cross carved by the fifteen-year-old who had finally had to stick heroin into his arm to find the mystery of his existence. In carving the cross he had found the mystery of the cross, the crossed arms that tell us we are only at the cross and it's in the impenetrable spaces where identity awaits us. Until then we have only the certainty of our own existence to believe in.

I stood in the rear of the Protestant church built out of

an old Jewish clothing store. The walls of the church were hung with religious paintings done by the children. A mural painted on brown wrapping paper that could have been painted by Giotto ran down the length of one wall. The big plate-glass storefront windows had been painted white. The ceiling was white. Emerson stood on a raised wooden platform that could be called an altar. About fifty children faced Emerson and they were singing "London Bridge Is Falling Down." But the children made it sound as though they were bringing down the gates of hell. Their voices were passionate, reaching into those regions where even the wisest men repeat one another. London Bridge Is Falling Down! I felt like joining the children. Their voices were incredible. They were thundering at the gates. What is London Bridge? they were singing, we need a bridge to God, a bridge out of here! The moment a child becomes conscious of God he wants to know why God hides from him.

Emerson swept his hands downward. The singing ended. The voices of the children still hopeful.

"The singing was great!" Emerson called out. "We're going to use this song in our production. For those of you who may not have heard the story of the show we're going to do, let me tell you about it. We're going to call our show *The Plague*. You all know what a plague is. A plague is a terrible sickness that can strike at a whole city, a town, a village, even a country, and it can hurt large numbers of people. The most terrible plague we know about is the Black Plague of London. Now, the Black Plague of London doesn't mean Negroes were involved, you understand that!"

The children laughed.

"You also know that with modern medicine we have conquered most of the plagues, though we still have to be careful when there is a flood, bad water, diseased animals and diseased people. We are going to sing in our show about the plague of ignorance. That will be the idea of our show. The story will go this way. Vivian Small from West 117th Street is going to play the leading role."

The children clapped.

"We are going to borrow one of the most ancient stories for our own story. One story that is told in every part of the world is the story of a little child who has been raised away from the world of men and who cannot speak, write or understand the ways of the world. The child isn't dumb. He isn't sick. The child isn't unable to learn. It's just that the child has been living in the woods, raised by animals or locked in a room for years and years where he has never been given the chance to learn to speak, to write or to read. All over the world people speak to one another, they have a language, even though there are still people who do not have a written language."

The children listened.

"But here in the United States, where we do have a written language, there are millions and millions of children who can't read or write the English language with real meaning and it is as though they have been tied by chains in a dark cave underneath the earth. We are going to sing about the plague of ignorance. For there is no greater plague and no plague which can be so easily swept from the earth, wiped out, if only we want to do it. Once ignorance is destroyed, it is destroyed forever. I am going to pass out a song that I want all of you to learn for our next practice meeting. This is a song about cakes that are coated with honey and the cakes are shaped in the letters of the alphabet. The idea of the song is that knowledge is sweet, learning is sweet, and when you take the sweet cakes of learning into your body you take the sweet cakes of knowledge into your body forever. Nothing can ever get rid of this knowledge. It is yours forever. And that is what we are going to sing about."

The afternoon sun lit the white walls. The Giotto paintings on the brown wrapping paper looked magnificent. The wooden cross caught and held the sun. The children stood up, reluctant to leave. Emerson sensed the mood. He called out to the children, "We're going to do one more chorus of 'London Bridge.' I want Vivian Small to start it off, and when it's over we'll go home."

Vivian Small stood up. She looked about ten. She wore a pink dress. She waited for a nod from Emerson and then in a high plaintive voice she began "London Bridge" as though London Bridge was Harlem and she was trying to pierce a dark cloud that kept God from seeing Harlem. She sang as though she knew that if only her voice could cut through the cloud to God he would be able to see what was hidden from all eyes but her own because nobody could see what she had seen at the age of ten in a city that had twenty million eyes. As she ended her chorus, the fifty children joined in, now singing as though they were massed in the Cathedral of St. John the Divine and if God didn't hear them, it was only because he had heard them before.

Emerson came up to me as the monsters left and said, "Let's get the hell out of this goddamn place and I mean it literally. When those kids sing they tear my balls out. Let's go up to 116th Street and get a drink."

"They make you think, your monsters," I said, "when they sing. I've always been amazed that music makes a person think more than literature."

"I called you about some real monsters," Emerson said as we left the church. "That voice of Vivian Small makes me want to find the man who produced her and beat him. Vivian Small lives in two rooms on West 117th Street with her mother and five brothers and sisters. Vivian has asthma—God's sickness, I call it. Her brothers and sisters have asthma. The mother is a pig. The father is a bastard who sleeps in a basement on 119th Street. These kids are all crazy, but no one believes it. They look too sweet. They must have looked sweet as you stood there watching them sing, their voices high and holy. But inside they're crazy. Their insides whirl around. They don't have a center. They have no one place where they know they belong. This church isn't their center, even if I'd like it to be their center. This isn't the Middle Ages. We don't have churches now as the center of life. Henry Adams said that kind of church ended in the thirteenth century. The church now is where we go to get away from life. The center of life in America now is where the money is. You can't insult a man with money in this country. You can't laugh at him for being ignorant. You can't yell at him for not sympathizing with poor black bastards or poor Greeks. But I didn't drag you up to Harlem to talk about people with money. You work for a guy who has fifty million dollars and you know what money is. But you don't know what happened last night, that probably never happened on any other night in Harlem or even your West Side."

"What happened?" I asked Emerson as we crossed West 114th Street. A hook-and-ladder rushed past us, turning into 113th Street.

"There's always a fire in Harlem," Emerson said, "and it's always the wrong fire. The whole place ought to be burned to the ground the way they did it in Cleveland, Ohio. I visited my sister in Cleveland when they did it. The city took all of the rotten blocks, emptied them of people, sealed them off and then burned them to the ground because there was nothing worth saving. New buildings rose almost Biblical-like on the burned-out ground. But the fires didn't burn out the crazy way the white people of Cleveland feel about the Negroes, that wasn't to be expected."

As we walked toward 116th Street I realized that Emerson was speaking to me as he wrote in his letters to S. T. West, hard, direct, no compromise. And as we sat down at a table with our glasses of bourbon, I knew why he had chosen me instead of a letter to West to sound out his feelings. With West he never received a reply: he was writing to the white man with no ears. But he wanted a reply from me.

Emerson said to me, "Jenny Beal tells me that one day she wants to hear what you don't say. She said she's never seen a face like yours where the words rush over it. Yet you don't say a damn thing. You know this?"

"I speak on occasion," I said.

"Good," Emerson said. "Maybe this is the occasion. Let me tell you what happened and for the time this doesn't go into any record, no reports, but just into you, all right?"

I nodded.

"God knows," Emerson said, "the only real secret we keep from one another is that we're all going to die."

Emerson looked at my face for one final affirmation of his intuition that he could trust me.

"I was alone in the church at about nine-thirty last night," Emerson said. "I heard the door open. I saw eight black boys come in. It was a gang. They had the gang look. The gangs here in Harlem look like the arms of an octopus. They stick out, they crawl, they twist in every direction, they grope, they enclose themselves in the gang leader, who is the center of the octopus. He controls their movements. The arms all extend from him. There are no gangs, only gang leaders. For the other members of the gang are dead, they're lifeless, they have no identity. You can never mistake the gang leader. He always walks like he's going up the steps of a gallows. The gang leader came up to me. He wore gray flannel pants with a Daks waistband, a blue oxford button-down shirt. 'What can I do for you?' I asked him. 'Nothing,' he said, 'nothing. We just came in. We want to join your church. How

do you join?' 'This isn't a church that you join,' I told
him, 'you just come in.' 'We're here,' he said, 'we're in
the church.' The gang sprawled over the seats, stretching
out on the seats. I said, 'The church isn't open now.' The
gang leader said, 'Don't give me that shit! Churches
never close their doors.' The gang leader looked between
eighteen and twenty. I had never noticed him on the
block, but I had seen other black boys like him. The
sullen face that could be intelligent if only it had intelligence. He seemed to have that raw instinct for intelligence which, if denied intelligence, turns into a murder-
ous hate.

"I said to him, 'We have a program here. It's for everyone, including the kids from two years up who come here
after school. If you want to join in, come around in the
afternoon. Right now I'm closing up because I have to
get home.' 'I said you're not closed,' the gang leader said
to me, 'just because we're in here.' I told him, 'This is
everybody's church, whoever belongs to this neighborhood can come in.' The gang leader spit in my face.

"I started to swing at him, which was foolish. Before I
could get my arms up, he had a knife in his hand, the
blade open, and he held the blade about five inches away
from my throat. 'Sit down, preacher,' he said to me,
'we're going to make this church holy, we're going to
make it so holy that we'll show up the holes in all the
other fucking churches.' He held the knife at my throat
as he spoke. He wasn't nervous. The knife didn't shake.
But there was a sadness in his eyes.

"I think if I could have broken away I would have

beaten him to death, even though I knew that what he wanted most in life was to be beaten to death. He had one of the gang members bring a chair over to me. He told me to sit down. He had another gang member stand over me with a knife. I saw the other gang members were getting a little sick around their eyes and frightened. And the gang leader sensed it. He was no fool. The gang leaders are never fools.

"The wooden cross above the altar was inescapable. We were in a church. We were under the protection of God. The gang leader whispered to a gang member. The gang member stared at him. The gang leader told him to get out and get going. He then turned to me and said, 'Open up your pants!' I said, 'Kill me first.' He said, 'If you say that again, you *will* get killed!' I said I wasn't going to open my pants. 'All right,' he cried out at me, 'I'll show you what churches are for in this goddamn neighborhood, you and your fucking churches, we'll make it into a fucking church!' The gang members stared at the gang leader. He took out a plastic bag of heroin. He held the heroin in the palm of his hand and sniffed the heroin into his body, into those parts of the body where heroin somehow links up with the infinite waste in man.

"In about ten minutes the gang member returned with a Negro girl who looked about fourteen. The gang leader brought her over to the center aisle facing the wooden cross. He took hold of the girl, lifted up her dress and pulled down her underpants. He told the girl to lie down on the floor. She hesitated. He said 'Lay down' in a voice that told her she would be thrown off a roof if she didn't lie down. The girl stretched out on the floor. I could see her body trembling. The gang leader pointed to the girl on the floor and said, 'This is one church where you know where your load is going. Right into the box. When your prick is in there, you know that nobody else is there with you. Let's start reaching God,' he said to his gang members, who didn't understand a word he was saying, but as he spoke he was certain that I understood every word and action of his.

"The first boy came forward. He was the youngest. He looked about twelve. He wore sneakers and dungarees. He stood in front of the girl, then he knelt down, getting on top of her, and she flexed her legs, spreading them wide apart, and he assumed a position on top of the girl as old as we can be. The two rocked back and forth without saying a word. When his body shuddered he got up. One by one they got on top of the girl. The gang leader was last. He made the girl turn on her stomach. He had her get up on her knees, her head was on the floor, resting on her arms. The gang leader entered her from the rear. When he was finished he came over to me and said, 'You're next!' I waited until he took his knife away from my throat before saying to him, 'You've had your party, now get out of here before I get Bellevue on the phone and have all of you chained to a wall.'

"The gang leader stared at me as though he was almost willing for me to call Bellevue and have him chained to a wall. I didn't get on top of the fourteen-year-old girl, who didn't dare lower her legs as the gang leader spoke. She held them flexed, open, waiting. The gang leader obviously didn't kill me.

"They left about eleven. The girl didn't say a word during the entire proceedings, neither did any of the other gang members speak. Only the gang leader and myself. The silence all through the sacrificial fucking, the silence of the gang leader when he left, the silence of it all, as though we had no words for what was happening, the silence disturbed me more than the fucking.

"I had an idea," Emerson said. "I thought the two of us could walk around this neighborhood and try to spot him. I thought the two of us, just you and me, could sit down with him, just as we're sitting, and try to find out what he had in mind when he told the girl to stretch out on the floor of the church. Maybe he knows a lot of things we don't know and that we ought to know if we are going to make decisions about him. Maybe he heard talk about this church that never came home to me. Maybe this church is seen as a fake. Sometimes I want this church to save Harlem, and by Harlem I mean the capital seat of the Negro in America and not this filthy place.

"I'm fascinated by the legend of the Lower East Side. I've been to the Lower East Side a hundred times. Now it's a Negro and Puerto Rican slum, with most of the Jewish people living in the cooperative buildings. But those old filthy East Side buildings which are worse than the buildings here in Harlem because the East Side was a slum from the day of its birth—those East Side buildings produced a fantastic social revolution. I don't see that kind of revolution happening in Harlem, for all of its talk. I understand the Jewish people of the Lower East Side invaded America. They seized strongholds where they could get into the garment business, into real estate. They took possession, they knew what the enemy held and they attacked the enemy day and night until they set up unions, businesses, colleges, hospitals, medical schools, law degrees, professional degrees, they fought so that their children grew up in a warrior class and when the children were old enough they were the ones who took possession of this city. For almost fifty years New York has been a Jewish city."

Emerson picked up his glass of bourbon.

"This is something the black man has never been able to understand," Emerson said. "Or if they were able to understand the Jewish victory, they were never able to imitate it. This is why the black man hates the Jews. This is why the Negro intellectuals hate the Jews. The black men hate the Jews because the Jews knew how to take power. It's for this same reason that the black man in New York hates the Puerto Ricans because the Puerto Rican man has learned to take power. In Chelsea, the Bronx, the Upper West Side, East Harlem, the Lower East Side, wherever businesses have been abandoned in these areas by the white man, the Puerto Rican man has moved in and taken over the business. For years the black man has complained about the domination of Jewish business people in black neighborhoods, yet when the Jewish merchants vacate their stores, it is the Puerto Rican man who takes possession. This has driven the black man into further despair. But more than despair, it has shown more clearly than anything else in American life how deep and sick the black hurt is. For if the black man cannot take possession of business when it is available, and if business is America, then he is more truly outside of American life than he really believes himself to be."

Emerson finished his bourbon. "I know what to do with this bourbon," he said, "but what am I to do with my blackness? I don't want to play games with the black boy who sniffed heroin in the church. I don't want to play games with S. T. West. I don't want to play games with Jenny Beal. I saw the way you acted at West's party. You weren't bored, you just didn't pay any attention to what you thought was useless.

"How do I start breathing again? That's all the black boy wants who sniffed heroin up his nose. That's all those monsters want who you heard singing. More than twenty of them have asthma. There's something oppressive in the air, something worse than the pollution that stinks up the New York air, there's an oppression that lies on your chest, that chokes you, that makes it impossible for you to answer your critics. Maybe that's the reason the black boy broke into the church and had his gang fuck that pathetic girl on the floor of the church. Maybe all he wanted was one loud clear unmistakable roar from God. But God didn't roar. How do you think he felt when God didn't roar, when nothing happened because a girl had been fucked on the floor of a church? More emptiness, more oppression. Maybe murder is the next thing he will turn to. Because in murder you have a corpse. S. T. West said that. You have a body that won't breathe again, won't dream again, won't speak, won't think, won't answer you, won't be able to hurt you by its silence. Because you gave it every chance to speak while it was alive and had the chance."

Emerson paused to give me every opportunity and chance to speak while I was still alive. In his gray sweatshirt and khaki pants he looked as if he had just come out of a classroom on the Harvard campus. But the Harvard classrooms wouldn't get around to Emerson until 1980, not until his talk had become digested, refined, swallowed up, rendered powerless, and Emerson knew this.

"Can you be a minister now?" I asked Emerson.

He stopped the bourbon that he was bringing up to his mouth and put the glass slowly down on the table.

"No," Emerson said, "not until I finish this bourbon." He swallowed the bourbon and said, "What in the hell made you say that? I can't be a minister now. I don't have any credentials."

"Would you be willing to go back to divinity school to get your credentials?"

"The only credentials I want are from the human race and not the Yale Divinity School."

"How much more time do you need to become a minister?"

"You're serious, aren't you?" Emerson said.

"Have you thought about going back to divinity school?"

"Of course I've thought about it. I'm like everybody

else, occasionally I get a sinking feeling that I want to be safe, protected, to have status, to have a job that will see me through a lifetime, a pension, recognition."

"I don't mean that!" I said in a voice that caused Emerson to stare at me.

"What *do* you mean?" Emerson asked, concern in his voice because probably for the first time in his life as he spoke to a white man he didn't know what the white man meant, what lay beyond his words.

"Why?" he asked. "Why divinity school?"

And then I told him. "Because we invented God. And if we don't go on inventing God, then God dies. Take a look at the Saturday edition of *The New York Times* when they list the advertisements of the sermons that are going to be preached on Sunday. You'll think the entire ministry has gone mad. The black ministers don't even preach. They've gone completely mad. I've heard more black ministers than you. The big black ministers want to run the United Nations, the U.S. Senate, the local school boards, they want to put an end to drug addiction, illegitimacy, welfare, retardation, the abandonment of black children, when all they know about these things is words. I know a famous professor who went to India to visit one of his pupils who received a doctorate in the social sciences. When he spoke to her in India, she spoke about the problems in India in the specialized language of the words she had learned at the Columbia University school of social work. He told me that it would take her fifteen years of work in India before she would understand the words she was using.

"The black ministers don't want to see and they don't want to understand. They don't see the whole world of failure that surrounds most of the Negroes in America. They don't see that this is now the most dangerous trap ever sprung on the Negro by white America. This is worse than the slave period in the South in the 1800's, worse than the North in the 1920's and '30's. They're afraid to see how many millions of children are being educated to an expectancy of failure. If you expect failure, you have a pretty good guarantee that you are going to achieve failure. This is the trap. You're one of the few people I've met who know this.

"Those Jews you talked about on the Lower East Side, they had no built-in expectancy of failure. They were after success and they got success. Why do you think that black boy fucked the girl on the floor of your church? He knew that if he fucked the girl on the floor of the church he had to succeed in his failure because fucking a girl on the floor of a church is failure pure and simple. He wasn't ready for the big failure or he might have killed you in the church. But he may come back to attack you if he has to go the entire route of failure. The only place for him to go is murder. Murder is absolute. More absolute than taking heroin or fucking girls. You can't continue to play around with these characters. You can't touch them. You can't reach them. You can't speak to them. There's no language between you and them, no bridge. The police can't handle them, the courts can't handle them, the institutions can't handle them, the psychiatrists are bewildered by them, the jails can't keep them all, the whole literature on delinquency is a literature of failure. There's a mountain of failure between you and them. You can't move that mountain of failure. It can only bury you. You can't play the stupid fucking games that social workers play. Their games are part of the failure, they're trained in failure, they expect failure, they have a special language for their failure, they can rationalize their failure in a thousand ways, they exist on failure. You'll be murdered if you try to play their games.

"But as a minister you don't have to play their games. The ministers who try to play the social-worker games are the ministers who get murdered. The ministers who try to play at being doctors, lawyers, psychologists, cure-alls, they're the ministers who succeed in failure because they want to fail, because they don't know anything else. But as a minister you don't have to play these games. You can be listened to. You need that final voice that you know is yourself, and if you don't get it soon, then these people will kill you."

"Both you and West talk about murder," Emerson said.

"And so do you," I told Emerson.

"I'm closer to it than you or West."

"What I'm talking about is not the kind of murder West is talking about, or maybe it is. I'm talking about the murder of ideas, faith, which is just about all that we've got to go on. I think you've been exposed to enough failure now. It's a good lesson to learn. But from now on it can only be repetition unless there's real change. Some people can thrive on repetition. But I think it will kill you. How many more Jenny Beals, how many more Harlem gangs, how many more phony white ministers, how many more phony black ministers, how many more W.A.S.P.'s do you have to tangle with? Their number is limitless."

"Why do you say all this to me out of all the blacks you've known?"

"Because you asked me and I'm seldom asked."

"Do you think I can make it as a minister?"

"I think you can."

"And you think being a minister for me is more important than being anything but a minister. Why?"

"Because the whole black-white world in the United States is insane. The black man won't listen to the white man and the white man won't listen to the black man. We pass laws to guarantee what's already in the Constitution and then everybody says the laws won't work. We live, all of us in the United States, in an expectancy of failure. That's our national disease. It haunts every man. I'm sick of what I see and what I know about the cities, and I can talk and write every day and no one will listen to me because we've learned how to swallow up one another. We're all losers, but we honor winners. A black man who can speak simply, directly, cutting through the insanity, who no longer finds it necessary to fuck girls on the floor of a church or to conceal his voice in public— that black man will be listened to. He'll be listened to by the blacks and whites because we're a nation of losers that honors winners."

"You're talking about a Christ that is a winner."

"We have a Christ, but we don't have a black man who speaks freely."

"Can I ask you another question that I have to get out?" Emerson said.

"Go ahead."

"Why does West think I'm going to get involved in a murder?"

"West is a technician. He's a criminal lawyer. He's a damn good criminal lawyer. He's a Protestant. He's a damn good Protestant. But he thinks death is the symbol of life. He thinks if he has a corpse to defend he can prove the desirability of life. He wants his moment to defend life, but he can't defend the life that he sees around him. He can only defend death. He's a hundred percent right. But who listens to him? What does West want? He wants to end the punitive laws that punish criminals instead of helping them. But it's only been two years since we stopped burning people in New York State in the electric chair. West has shifted a lot of his ideas about crime over to the world of the black man and the white man, and that is where he sees you. West thinks that if he can show why one good man was murdered and why the good man had to be murdered and if he can convince the court to free the murderer, then he will have resolved one of the great dilemmas facing us. You're right. This is the Christ legend. But we've already had our Christ. This is why West thinks you're going to be involved in a murder, because you live in a neighborhood of violence. And because of all the people he has met in his vast and varied career—and West has spent a lifetime surrounding himself with people—of all the people he has met, he has told himself that you are the one person who can supply him with the most arguments for the presentation of his case. I think it would be fascinating to sit in a courtroom and listen to West unfold his case, but I don't think it's worth your life. Because West will only be speaking to ears that don't listen."

"And do you think I can speak so somebody will listen?" Emerson asked.

"I think you should only talk to people who can still listen, like those kids singing 'London Bridge Is Falling Down.' They listened. They were singing about the fall of Harlem and you know it. Forget the others like that grown monster sticking heroin into his nose and fucking that poor girl on the floor of your church. He's dead. You can't touch him, reach him, get him to feel, he's dead, out of reach of anybody's ears or voice."

"How can I be a minister and forget him?" Emerson asked me.

"Because the living dead like him will soon become the special province of government. We're building up to a mass employment of superfluous people. The Federal government is going to have to absorb these dead bodies. A great big impersonal bureaucracy can absorb dead bodies, but an individual can't. Look at the department of welfare in this insane city. It has over 650,000 people living in filth, and every day of the week the social workers punch their time clocks as though they are working for General Motors. How long do you think these social workers could last if they saw the filth, if they heard the voices of their clients? They can only absorb the dead bodies, they can't do anything for the living people."

"Tell me one more thing," Emerson said. "Did West ever show you any letters I wrote to him?"

"No," I said. S. T. West had marked the letters privileged and confidential and I didn't think it would hurt to lie after having told so much of the truth.

Emerson stood up. He stood at the table, making it clear that he didn't expect me to get up with him. He leaned across the table and said to me, "West picked me to die. And you're picking me to live. I'm going out for a walk to see what kind of a say I have in the matter. I'll see you," Emerson said, "I'll see you."

WHY BOTHER with superfluous details?" This is what Emerson wrote to me, addressing his letter "Dear John Brooks" instead of "Dear White Man With No Ears." I was grateful for the recognition. The letter arrived on Friday morning, two days after I sat with Emerson on West 116th Street.

I have always been frightened by that terrible cry from the Crusades when a Christian king surrounded an infidel town and one of the knights said to the king, Sire, there are Christians in the walled city, what should we do? And the king replied, Kill them all! God will know the difference! When I left you on 116th Street I walked out into 116th Street and Lenox to see if it was still possible for me to tell the difference. I didn't like what you said about the living dead in Harlem, which means the living dead everywhere in America.

You spoke so convincingly and out of so much experience, as though you had been to the land of the living dead, which I am sure you have, for you are one of the few white men I have met who has made that terrible journey into the homes that even the black people have obscured from themselves.

Where did I go? I went in search of that eighteen-year-old boy. I knew he lived somewhere in the neighborhood of the church and if I walked long enough and stood long enough on the street, I would find him. When I walked out into 116th Street I felt the earth under my feet for the first time since I was a boy in the country outside of Baltimore where I never knew the white men who lived there. It's strange and terrible the way the earth is hidden in New York. West 116th Street is an ugly street. It is so ugly that for the first time I stared at it in disbelief. You only see black people on 116th Street. It is their possession, our possession and what terrible things we have done with it. Even if we inherited the ugliness, we have left the ugliness untouched.

I looked for the eighteen-year-old boy on West 117th Street. I walked from Eighth Avenue to Third Avenue with my eyes wide open and they have never been more open! If only the windows were washed. If only the sidewalks were swept. If only the brass were polished. If only flowers were planted in windowboxes as they are on East 75th Street. Is that so difficult? Of course it is. Can you tell a man with a broken leg to run? Everywhere I saw garbage cans. Everywhere the garbage cans overflowed. Isn't the garbage picked up on West 117th Street? Doesn't anyone complain? Is there so much food on West 117th Street that the garbage cans have to overflow? No wonder the advertisements in the Harlem papers stress *incinerator*. The word is a clue to those who want to escape from the garbage cans. Why can't the garbage cans be emptied daily, promptly, washed down, removed from the sidewalk and the gaze of children who are trying to force a childhood on themselves? You know that the smartest black people tell you, I never had a childhood. Can you think of a more terrible phrase?

I didn't see the eighteen-year-old on West 117th Street. I did see the gangs of addicts at Madison Avenue and 115th Street. That is the ugliest street in New York. Why is it ugly? Because the human face is empty on 115th Street. That is why we find the faces of retarded children ugly and why we weep when we see a retarded child smile or try to pronounce a word he has never spoken before.

I looked everywhere for the eighteen-year-old. I entered a building on 118th Street and climbed the stairs to the roof and went across the roofs looking for him. The roofs are where the gangs play their games. Heroin is injected and eleven-year-old girls become pregnant.

At nine o'clock in the dusk I saw him standing on the corner of West 114th Street alone as though he was waiting for me, for he smiled at me as though we had entered into a conspiracy. "Can we talk?" I said to him. First he said, "Do you want to get laid?" Then he said, "In about three minutes a guy is going to come by for a package from me, after that we'll see."

Why did I want to see him? Now I can understand West's fascination with crime. The criminal is ruthless in the pursuit of his satisfaction. Ordinary men are fascinated by ruthlessness and frightened of ruthlessness. An artist is ruthless. A religious man is ruthless. Children are ruthless. The eighteen-year-old was ruthless in his pursuit of emptiness. Forget the eighteen-year-old sticking heroin in his nose, you said, he's dead, out of reach of anybody's voice. I couldn't forget him. I stood patiently on the corner of West 114th Street while he negotiated the sale of a packet of heroin for $15.

Why was the gang leader the last one to enter the girl on the floor of the church and not the first?

When he pocketed the $15 for the heroin, he said, "Where to?" and we started walking toward 110th Street and Central Park to the benches. He said, "If we sit here some fucking patrol car will pull up and grab us for playing with each other on the bench and it'll cost us $25 to convince them otherwise." "Then let's walk," I said and he agreed. But he said, "Let me pick the blocks so that we don't get our heads kicked in." He turned us toward Fifth Avenue.

"Well?" he asked.

What was I to say? How do you ask an eighteen-year-old boy if he is a representative of the living dead? How do you determine if he is beyond economic redemption? If he is only eighteen and if he has a life expectancy of sixty-nine years, how do you ask him what he will do with fifty-one years of emptiness? Eternity sounds like a lesser time. Could he be trained as a male nurse? Could he be trained to be an IBM programmer? Could he be trained to be a lawyer? Could he be trained to do any one of the jobs that twentieth-century America finds necessary for carrying out its manifest destiny? Could we isolate this one eighteen-year-old boy and rescue him? Has the test

ever been made? Or was he no longer a HE but a symp-
tom, as you say, out of reach, out of mind, the living
dead, infected, diseased, broken off from all humanity,
only living until he died alone, except that there were
tens of thousands like him.

I said to the boy, "Do you read much?" He said, de-
fensively, as though I had asked him if he could breathe,
"I read, I can read every goddamn word in the English
language even if I don't know what they all mean. I had a
teacher who was a nut on phonetics and sounding out
words."

All the words in the English language were available to
him!

Are all of the words in the English language the sum
grand compilation of what we know or is there something we know beyond what anyone has been able to
write down? The earliest writers, Homer and the rest, they
were able to create stories beyond what any collective intelligence knew. How else could their stories have lived
so long? Why are we still excited by Homer and why are
his images so pure? Why do we still accept the Bible as
the word of God? What words could make the eighteen-
year-old acceptable to life?

I asked the eighteen-year-old, "What was the last book
you read?"

He said, "I was walking on 124th Street near Lexington Avenue where the Goodwill store is. They were
throwing out a bunch of broken toys, broken furniture,
dirty clothes, stuff they couldn't repair or sell. I know the
Goodwill store because my mother dressed me from its

clothing bins for ten years. There was a pile of people in front of the Goodwill, mostly old men and black women with their babies and some Puerto Rican mothers and their babies. They were fighting to get this dirty broken crap, digging into the big barrels, coming up with stuff like it was treasure, and it looked like one of those scenes in the movies where somebody throws bread to a lot of people and they fight in the dirt for it. You ought to try and make that scene any day around twelve o'clock. It'll make you vomit, except for one thing. Those black mothers and those Puerto Rican mothers are digging in the barrels to find toys for their kids. You see the kids going away with a broken fire-engine truck, broken bats, one kid carried away a great big broken Garzola that probably needed fifteen batteries at twenty cents apiece to make it work. In one of those barrels I saw a bunch of books. Laying on the sidewalk I saw a book about Genghis Khan. I took it. I read it that afternoon in Mount Morris Park just around the corner from the Goodwill. That's the park where you can get a bag of junk quicker than a Good Humor ice cream. A cop watched me reading—like I was a faggot waiting for business. Genghis Khan couldn't read or write and he never got off a horse except to get fucked, but he conquered the world and he was an old man when he died. Which is something Henry the Eighth wasn't when he died. That was another book from the Goodwill pile. Did you know that Henry the Eighth had priests roasted over hot coals? That he had priests ripped to pieces, that he had the arms and head and cock cut off of priests while he sat and watched it being done and while he ate chicken? He had priests chained to a pole for twenty-eight days and when they lived through it he had their arms cut off and then their legs, so that they could see it being done to them if they still cared. Genghis Khan killed people, but he kept alive the people he needed, he never killed an engineer. That was the last book I read, the story of Genghis Khan."

What a remarkable statement!

We were on 96th Street and Fifth Avenue. He said, "Do you feel like a bus ride?" We caught a Fifth Avenue bus going to Washington Square. He took the window seat. "I take this bus maybe once a month," he told me, "I take it when I feel like flying. I ride it clear down to the last stop. Down through all this territory, past these lighted windows. I look into these windows. These glass windows hide what I'm never going to have, not unless I take it like the Khan, killing the poor fucking doormen because they're in the way and then going through the apartments like the Khan going through Europe. That's what I see on the bus down to Washington Square. Then when I get to 8th Street I get out and I see the black faggots in the park, those beautiful black faggots who don't look human any more. I get one of them to take me up to his pad on a street like MacDougal Street and before the bastard can get down on his knees I kick him in the belly, I beat the bastard because his beautiful black body is going to waste when he walks like a freak in Washington Square Park. You know the faces of those faggots, they look like dead men. Yet they're the most

204

beautiful men to come out of the black mothers. How can a black mother raise a beautiful black boy and then see him become a faggot?"

"Why do you take heroin?" I asked the eighteen-year-old.

"I don't take it," he said. "I grew up with it. I've been on the stuff since I was thirteen."

At 50th Street as we passed the Gothic towers of St. Patrick's Cathedral he ended the Gothic version of his life, a life that never had a beginning. Washington, D.C., now finds his life more bewildering than the Norman farmers found the Gothic arch when they first entered Chartres.

When we got to Washington Square he said we could sit on a park bench without worrying about the law because most of the guys on the benches were faggots. Whatever he said was against a framework of law. This is West's insight. Have you ever heard an eight-year-old child in Harlem say *The Cops!* as though all hell was opening under his feet?

In his blue oxford button-down shirt and gray slacks the eighteen-year-old looked as though Washington Square was his natural habitat. But his natural habitat was emptiness. He told me that he had never seen his father, which wasn't unusual. He told me that when he was born his mother was on heroin and for the first few weeks of his life he was a drug addict until the hospital detoxified him. He told me that when he was nine years old his mother was sent to the Women's House of Detention on Christopher Street for fifteen days. He said his mother was drunk and half crazy from caring for the five kids in the house. She started screaming at the police, God fuck you all, God put a pistol to my head, and he tried to pull her away from the police, but she started to rip at the faces of the police and they dragged her along the street into the squad car, which is where she really wanted to be, in jail, to get a rest away from her children.

He told me that when he was eleven his mother had syphilis. They lived on West 103rd Street then in a filthy welfare building and he heard screaming every night of his life there and most of the nights he had to sleep in the hallway while his mother took on customers when her welfare check ran out. He told me that one of his mother's customers tried to rape him, and his mother hit the customer on the head with a meat cleaver which she kept on the table for such emergencies. He said: "When I was eleven my mother had sores all over her face. Dark blotches. It was a Wednesday afternoon. I was just home from school on 105th Street. I was walking with my mother. A white guy in a blue suit stopped her on West 103rd Street and said, Are you Mrs. Helene Williams? My mother said yes. He said that he was from the United States Public Health Service and they had a card on my mother saying she had syphilis and she wasn't keeping her appointments. He asked her if she wanted to go downtown for an examination. He said his car was there on 103rd Street. Then he noticed me. He asked my mother who I was. She said, He's my son. He said, Where does he sleep? My mother said, He sleeps alongside me in bed. He said, We have to examine the boy. My mother screamed at him, You can't touch him, you can't take blood from him, you're not going to take blood from him, he doesn't have it. The Public Health man said I had to have a test to see if I was infected. I heard him tell a guy alongside him that my mother had infected 150 guys in the neighborhood, according to their record of contacts. The Public Health guy said my mother didn't have to worry about them taking me away, I could be tested in the neighborhood. My mother said no. The guy kept arguing with my mother and finally he said he would get the police if she didn't cooperate. My mother said all right. The guy from the Public Health had been questioning a bunch of winos who hung out in a basement on 103rd Street where they got cheap booze and syphilis along with it when they drank from the same bottle. He took me into that cellar for the test. I will never forget it and I will never let anyone else forget it. It was a deep cellar. I've been back there a hundred times since that afternoon. The winos are still there, the filth is still there, nothing has changed except some of the winos have died and others have taken their place. The cellar has a great big coal furnace. In the back were the bins for coal. You could taste the coal dust. The whole fucking cellar was lit by one bulb near the furnace. There was a bench close to the furnace. The guy from the Public Health took out a kit. He took out a rubber tube. He started to roll up my shirt sleeve. He tied the tube around my arm. Then he had a needle to suck the blood out of me. The blood that had to be tested for the germs that traveled from my mother to me in the same bed where she fucked all those men she had infected. When my mother saw the needle she became hysterical. She lunged at the guy from the Public Health Service. She screamed at him, Get out of here, you fucking white bastard, you fucking white pig, you're not going to take any blood from this boy, he doesn't have it, I know he doesn't have it, get out, get out before you get killed. They didn't take blood from me. When my mother calmed down she took me on her own for a blood test. I didn't have syphilis. But the sores kept getting bigger and bigger on her face and there was a stink from her body. My mother never got rid of her syphilis. She was buried with it. She got into a drunken fight with a drunken black super on 103rd Street. He picked up an iron pipe wrench and beat my mother over the head with the pipe wrench. I saw her on West 103rd Street with her head smashed open and this black pig standing there saying he didn't mean to kill my mother."

It was now useless to ask the boy why he had entered the church and entered the fourteen-year-old girl on the floor. But I did anyway, to see what new terrors could be unleashed.

I remember now, John Brooks, from all of my reading at Harvard one line that haunted me when I read it: If a man is sick, is unable, is mean-spirited and odious, it is because there is so much of his nature which is unlawfully withholden from him.

Is any statement more true of the eighteen-year-old? What was withholden from that boy? Before birth, even before his birth, he was denied a proper birth. His mother was a narcotic addict. He was delivered into the

world as an infant already addicted to drugs. He had no
father. A man impregnated his mother, but he never saw
the man. His mother took him from Metropolitan Hospital to a filthy room on West 114th Street where there
was no private toilet, no cooking and no room for a crib
and he had to sleep in a single bed with his mother. Even
in the remote villages of Outer Mongolia there is water, a
mother, a father to bring food and smiles to his newborn
son. From birth, life was withholden from him. When he
was two his mother had a breakdown and she went into
Rockland State Hospital, but that didn't prevent her
from having four more babies, three of whom had to be
placed in institutions. The eighteen-year-old went from
foster home to foster home while his mother was at
Rockland State. He could never be placed for adoption
because of his history of drug addiction. Such babies rot.
I suppose you know that we were able to pass laws preventing cruelty to animals long before we were able to
pass laws preventing cruelty to children. After eighteen
years of existence he came into my church two nights
ago.

This is what he said to me. "We were on the roof at
115th Street on top of the building where the junkies
break into basements at night to sleep and where maybe
fifty to sixty of them sleep on that filthy concrete floor. I
don't even call them junkies any more. They're the junk-
heaps. Garbage. We were on the roof, the eight of us,
wondering what to do, with the sun down on the roof
and the screams of the junkies coming up the airshaft.
Sometimes the police come to cart them off, but the po-

lice don't know what to do with them. I heard a cop say
one day, shoot all the bastards. Maybe one day they'll try
it. The guys with me didn't know what to do with themselves. They always look to the leader. I was the leader.
They looked to me. I joined my first gang when I was six
years old. I got beat up on 117th Street and I was afraid
to go out of the house. The gang I joined had one block
that they owned, where they felt safe. All the rest of the
world was a danger to them. They were scared and they
were ignorant. That's what makes a gang so dangerous.
They don't know what responsibility is. They never had a
chance to learn. Nobody ever let them be responsible.
The gang is just protection from all the dangers of the
world. I know one thing in this world—what a gang is—
and it's the most useless information in the world to
know.

"We were on the roof five flights above those stinking
bodies in the basement where you don't know who is living or who is dead. You have to see that scene one night.
We were on the roof. What were we doing? Lester
Charles was playing with his balls. Donald Borden was
sleeping. Three other guys were just sitting around. They
all look to me. When you're the leader you've got to
lead. I said, Let's go to the fucking church on 112th
Street. They didn't say, For what, why, what're we going
to do there? They just got up because I said let's go and
it was a place to go. I don't know why I said let's go to
your church except that I passed your church around two
o'clock and saw that wooden cross nailed on the wall and
it made me think how I would feel if some pigs nailed

my hands and feet to a cross and left me there to die. I
sometimes think that all we want is an easy way of dying.

"Inside of the church I studied that cross. Inside of the
church I got suspicious of the way the gang was feeling
about me bringing them into a church. You can't have a
gang suspicious of you, not if you're the leader. Even if
all of them put together don't have the brains of a dog,
you can't have them suspicious of you. That's the rule.
So I had Donald Borden bring in that girl, Doris Evans,
who we all get into when there's nothing else to do. Even
when I sent for her I didn't think in my own mind that
we were going to gang-rally her on the floor of the
church. Now I think if Christ was alive he would try to
fuck her to bring some kind of sense in her head. We
never know if Christ fucked anyone. Can you imagine
him with a woman? I think you should have fucked Doris
Evans on the floor of your church, that's a chance you'll
never have again in your life.

"When Doris Evans came into the church there was
something about the cross that said nail her to the floor. I
watched the others on her, the eight of them, and you
know what kind of fucking that is, in and out until you
drop a little load. Doris Evans could take fifty guys that
way. I waited to be the last to get in her. I got into her
from the back so that I wouldn't be in her the way the
others were. My hands were wet when I got into her. Her
body was hot and cold when I touched her. She trembled
like a sick dog. Then for the first time in years I felt as if I
might be doing something wrong, instead of thinking as I
usually do that everything wrong was right. I thought

211

that when my cock slid into her I would hear a cry from the roof of your church. Didn't a cock crow for Christ? The deeper I went into her the more silent everything became. It seemed I was the only person in the world breathing. And then when I came, when I began to go off in her, when I began to empty myself, I knew I was left behind. I didn't go off anywhere inside of Doris Evans. I was still me. I was nothing. I left six hundred million eggs in Doris Evans. That scared me. That's why we got out of your church so fast. Because as I slid out of Doris Evans I thought I could feel one of the six hundred million eggs making that journey to where her eggs lay waiting and in nine months from the time on the floor she would be in Metropolitan Hospital delivering a baby. I didn't want that baby added to the population of the world. That would be too much of a joke for me. We got Doris Evans out of that church into a toilet, where we scrubbed out her insides. I even bought her a douche bag that she never used before in her life and I had her soak her insides out ten times with vinegar until there wasn't a chance that an egg would stay alive. But out of six hundred million eggs you never know.

"I thought about you all that night. I couldn't get to sleep. I thought, What was that minister boy thinking when he saw all of us going into Doris Evans on the floor of his church and did he think that God was going to send thunderbolts into the church? Or didn't he know that God lets us play by our own rules? As crazy as it sounds to you, my mother and me used to talk a lot about God. We'd talk in that bed where she fucked everyone when her welfare checks ran out because God is about the only real person in this world for most black people. Now, black boy, what did you think when you saw me and Doris Evans fucking on the floor of your church?"

What mysteries life has! How unfixed everything is! How dazzling we humans are! How wonderful when we tell the truth to one another! What discoveries still lie inside of us! Certainly we can approach a time when we'll no longer be afraid of one another! How much more we have to learn even though we think we know everything! If only we can now learn not to be frightened! But how is this to be brought about? This boy spoke to me. He can read. He can listen. He is not so dead that he can't live again. But what is he to do?

Do you know where I left him? On West 115th Street, where he lives. We rode the Eighth Avenue subway back to 116th Street. It was about two in the morning. I walked him back to the house where he lives. Is there such a house in New York? Of course there is. I saw it! He said to me, Do you want to see the addicts? I said yes. The building was in ruins, yet it was filled with families. The front door was kicked out. The tiles were ripped off the walls. Down here, the eighteen-year-old said. He opened the basement door. We went halfway down the flight of stairs. There in front of us were men piled up on the floor sleeping next to one another for warmth, piled up as though they were all born dead. There was a terrible stink from the basement. A cold dirty wet stink. The boy closed the door as soon as he saw that I saw the bodies piled on the floor. I followed him up the steps, out of breath, out of mind. But those men who stick needles in their arms to stay alive, they all must sleep somewhere!

It is useless for me to attempt to tell you more about this boy's life. What is important is that he is life!

Of my own life, I will soon know if I dare to become part of the God that judges us only after we have lived.

Thomas Emerson

I STOOD for an instant in front of the flower beds of Rockefeller Center watching the dazzling spectacle of Fifth Avenue at 6:15 in the evening. It was a brilliant September day. No one in my memory had ever been murdered at Fifth Avenue and 50th Street. Here the New York crowds rushed majestically toward anonymity. Only a fraction of them were ever physically murdered. This was the open-air temple of New York and S. T. West knew it, which was probably why he asked me to meet him in such an improbable place as the lounge on the sixty-fifth floor.

No one could deny the greatness of Fifth Avenue. Its buildings rose to enclose the individual in the vision of its architects, which was to draw customers into the stores. The airline offices were beginning to look like tombs waiting to be discovered by future archaeologists. Fifth Avenue was a solid mass of buildings. Banners hung from the buildings. Nothing gives style to a street like waving banners. On the west side of Fifth Avenue at 59th Street, Central Park began its existence, an extraordinary vision that had been purchased for $18,000,000. And today, like all the great sensible visions of men, it was beyond price.

Civilization does have a safety valve in not giving a price to those things that it honors the most. From where I stood, everything had a price. For ten cents the crowds hurrying toward the subways and buses could buy the news of the double murder on West 93rd Street. But only the aged would be frightened by the double murder. The aged knew they were being slowly murdered by a generation that had no use for them. I watched the crowds and hoped for an instant of clarity, such as I had seen during the 1964 eclipse of the sun, when from the roof at 53rd and Fifth I watched the sky open and reveal a depth and clarity I never dreamed existed in the sky. How fantastic to see the sky. How fantastic to see a dead body.

I went to the sixty-fifth floor and ordered a martini and waited for West. When he didn't arrive by the second martini, I got up to telephone his apartment, only to realize I didn't have his unlisted telephone number. I ordered a third martini. How fantastic existence must seem to a man like West who would like to do everything right!

The sky of New York began to roll back, and from the sixty-fifth-floor window the sky opened into bands of red, blue and gold, colors from the ash of a volcanic explosion in the Pacific. They were deep pure colors, as pure as the colors discovered by the twelfth-century monks at St. Denis, colors lost to the world for eight hundred years. The St. Denis monks made a blue that no artist has ever been able to imitate. This blue, this clarity, was in the sky on the cold chill October morning when the Pope actually descended from the sky over New York. Within minutes the Pope was actually driving through Harlem. What if he had held a Mass in a rubbish-strewn lot on West 117th Street? Would it have made a difference to the seven hundred thousand people in Harlem? The difference is in ourselves. How could the Pope grasp the horror with which we view one another? One man in American history, coming from another shore, had grasped the horror. He observed it in its beginning before we even knew the horror we had started. Nothing in subsequent history has ever shaken the observations of the Frenchman.

I listened for the phone to ring on the sixty-fifth floor. I moved my drink over to the phones. But all I heard was Charles Eaton and myself talking over breakfast in his office this same morning, and my saying to Eaton: "Charlie, you ask me what I think when I think to myself. Two nights ago I was talking to a producer friend on East 83rd Street. He asked me what I thought about this 'black crap.' We're now going into a period where we are beginning to hate the black man as much as some people used to love the black man when he was in isolation. This was the substance of what my friend on East 83rd Street had to say: 'We're coming to the instant when the middle class in America will have no place to run or hide from the black population. In cities like Cleveland, Chicago, Detroit, Los Angeles, San Francisco, where people hide from one another, this is already happening. Some of the middle-class families have already made two and three costly moves away to escape the black population.

Now they can't move again. There is no place to move, they can't afford to move. The land for building is gone. The distances to travel to work are too great. The horror of having to move again is too great. But the horror of having to live with black people is greater. What's going to happen? The great white middle class which is America will begin to look for a leader to take them out of their horror. A leader who will rise up and say, Don't run from this black horde, destroy them, you have the power, the police, the guns, you own the country, don't run, fight. But can the middle class in America fight? We'll see, we'll see one day soon,' my producer friend said. 'One day soon we may see the countryside dotted with chimney stacks and civil servants going off to work in the camps. What will you do then?' he asked me, and ended by saying, 'and the Negroes talk about destroying the whites.' The Negroes can only bring about sporadic terror, Charlie. If the terror becomes too great, then we will really see bloody fighting, the final isolation of Negroes. We're ignorant about death. It's our ignorance about death that gives such persuasive power to the idea of killing people if you want to get rid of them. It's a solution that still haunts us nationally and internationally. This, Charlie, can actually happen if the great American white middle class decides in its collective wisdom that it will not continue to run from the black man and that it has run out of places to run to. What can stop it? Not law. Law will only make it happen. I don't know anything or anybody that can stop it from happening except the American people, and I mean the American people both black and white." That was the end of my speech to Charles Eaton.

I got up from the table and my third martini to telephone the 24th police precinct, where I knew the captain in charge. I thought West might have taken a detour to the sixty-fifth floor by stopping in at the precinct house to see the two boys who had committed the murder. The captain told me that he had not seen West since the afternoon investigation on West 93rd Street, but West had telephoned him since then, just about an hour ago, to ask for the address of the two boys who had committed the elevator murders. The captain gave me the address, and when I heard him mention West 118th Street I descended the sixty-five floors and rushed to get a taxi.

WHEN I GAVE the cab driver the Harlem address, he stepped up the speed of his cab and roared toward West 118th Street while there was still dusk. "Are you a detective?" he asked me. I said no. "Can I ask you what you're going to West 118th Street for?" he said. I don't know, I don't know, I said in a muffled voice, which he didn't hear. All the pure gold, the pure blue, was gone from the sky. The cab rumbled and roared past doormen who didn't know of the existence of the eighteen-year-old who contemplated cutting their throats to gain entry to the apartments. "Did you hear about those two old people who got killed?" the cab driver asked. Yes, I told him. "In my building I don't ride the elevators. I live in the Bronx. There's a B on our elevator and that B button takes you down into the basement two floors below the street level and you never know what kind of a son of a bitch is down there pressing the B button to get you. This goddamn city. We need a cop on every subway train, on every bus, on every elevator, in every toilet, in every taxi after ten o'clock. What's going on?" he asked me. "You know what's going on? We're all nuts, I think this stinking pollution is affecting our brains. New York was never like this. But now this pollution is stinking up the air, softening up our brains. In London one day four thousand people dropped dead from the pollution. Here we just rot. I read in the *Times* that the pollution makes you tired, heavy, exhausted, your brain can't work. I keep all of my windows closed when I'm working Fifth Avenue because there the fumes can kill you. I'm thinking of wearing some kind of a mask. But what good is a mask when two punks can kill you in an elevator? Not even punks, but babies."

We went past 112th Street where the dazzling wooden cross hung. Where Emerson had seen how demanding God can be. Where the young monsters sang "London Bridge Is Falling Down"—if only it would. We were entering the impenetrable soil of America, the virgin soil, the virgin soil of American Negro life, the soil in which the Negro had assumed that if he planted his feet he would grow. Survive, yes, but grow? Not in the American soil. But seeds are the most extraordinary form of life, dormant, lifeless, but yet life itself.

I felt a cold chill as we neared West 118th Street. The air was filled with sirens. The sirens never leave Harlem. There is always a fire. Always a police siren. There were police sirens all around us. I could see the flashing red lights whirling by. I could hear the sirens screaming that deliverance was coming. Who else was being murdered! Not West! I had felt in the phone booth sixty-five floors above the cold sidewalk that West was rushing to his death when I heard he had gone to West 118th Street to see the parents of the two boys who had murdered Mr.

and Mrs. Reid. I had no reason for the fear. Just a cold chill that still didn't leave me. That stayed with me from the almost forgotten days of World War II when I saw men rush to get killed because they could no longer tolerate existence. Why had West rushed up to West 118th Street? What could West do on West 118th Street except once again offer his services as a lawyer? Except this time he had seen the victims, this time he had been part of the murder and he had almost been a victim himself, he had opened the elevator door on the dead bodies, he had seen the dead bodies in their first minutes of death, in that longest journey, he had seen the two boys within minutes of their remorseless murder and he knew he was part of the murder. Two boys aged fourteen and fifteen do not beat an aged couple to death in an elevator in the middle of the afternoon unless they have the backing of an entire civilization that tells them this is what they must do to keep themselves alive. What could West say to the parents, what could he learn from the parents except that they had never thought the boys would ever do such a thing? But the thing was done, murder. No one ever contemplates murder except the murderers, who spend all of their lives preparing for their act of murder. And if it's a child who spends all of his waking days contemplating murder, the child has been murdered long before he commits his act of murder. West could change the circumstances. He was powerless once the act was committed. He could only arrive as an emissary from the other world.

I felt the cold chill that wouldn't leave me, a cold chill

that told me West wanted to be hurt, thrown down the stairs at West 118th Street, thrown off the roof, to find himself face to face with all of the horror that wasn't horror when someone else told it to you, that became horror only when it happened to you, otherwise it wasn't horror but just another truth that somehow had to be endured.

The sirens didn't stop screaming as we turned into West 118th Street. Above the scream of the police sirens and the fire engines I heard the screams of ambulances. I almost screamed myself as I pushed forward in the taxi and looked through the windshield at the ugliness of West 118th Street, a screaming ugliness, dirty, gutted, rotten, the place from which the two murderers aged fourteen and fifteen in an effort to find a father had walked twenty-five city blocks to murder Mr. and Mrs. Reid. The whirling red lights of the squad cars blocked West 118th Street at Eighth Avenue. The ambulances had gotten through and I saw the drivers in white jackets hurry into the building where West had gone. The address was in my wet hand. It never left my mind. I knew the building. I had seen the families in it from the top floor to the bottom floor, the ground floor with tin plates nailed to the walls to keep out the rats. And on none of the faces in the entire building would there be a sign of recognition of what West wanted to do or say. For that sign of recognition lasts only for the first few months of life and then is gone if denied. Was West gone, dead? Like Hamlet a victim of more murders than his own? Dead on West 118th Street? With eyes staring at his body, not knowing whether to weep or rejoice? I would know as soon as I got past the stoop, past the ugly doorway, past the spilled-over garbage, into the hallway, up to wherever West had gone. No policeman stopped me as I rushed up the stairs. There were police everywhere, their hands on their guns, ready to add to whatever murders had been committed.

I went upward to the second landing, toward the crowd of white jackets, the white pants legs hiding the body on the floor. And as I moved closer I saw it was West, dead as he had wished, his soul already on its way toward those first moments when we learn if it is life that we have lived.

There were no bruises on West, no knife wounds, none of the final holes that bullets make, there was nothing on West's face but the look of death and what he had carried with him into death—astonishment.

"How did he die?" I asked the men in white jackets, white pants.

"We think a heart attack," said one of the white jackets. We think a heart attack because it seemed inconceivable that a white man could die on the second-floor landing of a building on West 118th Street of anything but murder. But now a doctor moved in past us, a doctor with a black bag, a policeman hovering over him, as though to make certain that the heart attack wasn't murder. The doctor stayed at West's chest, he went to his face, his hands traveled over his body, and the doctor stood up to say, "I think it was a heart attack." Yes, it was a heart attack.

Out from behind the white jackets, the white pants, the police with their guns, the doctor rising with his black bag, in a voice that knew death, the mother—who else could she be?—the mother of one of the boys who had committed the murder, Mrs. Mills, said, loudly, talking to the police, the ambulance men, the doctors, the homicide men who were coming up the stairs, the neighbors who knew this was why they kept their doors closed behind inch-thick iron police locks, her voice, in the thick rising cadence partly of New York, partly of Georgia, mostly of death, Mrs. Mills said, "He came to my door. He said he was a lawyer. He said my boy had killed a man and his wife in an elevator on West 93rd Street. He said he wanted to help me. But I only screamed. I screamed for my baby boy who he said was a murderer. I screamed, I couldn't stop myself from screaming. He started back from the door. I saw his face go dark, there was no breath in him, no life in his eyes, his hands went grabbing at his eyes like he wanted to take away what he saw and then he dropped, falling away, his body rolling, falling dead, dead, when I touched him he was dead. I couldn't give him water. I couldn't give him help. He was dead."

EMERSON ·

TEN DAYS before he died West told me, "Most murderers don't have a problem with a victim. They kill the person closest to them. Their wives, girl friends, mothers, fathers, children, neighbors, employers. But Emerson's biggest problem is his choice of a victim. He wants to reveal himself. But the act of revelation requires a beholder. Maybe you'll become the beholder or the beholden for Emerson. Most of us aren't prepared to listen to the deepest truths from a friend about himself or even to hear our wives, our children or our parents talk in such a way that we know there is no escape from seeing them as mortal. Art does this. It forces our attention. But art doesn't last. Emerson had his theory about the murder of Kennedy. Let me give you my theory about the murder of Malcolm X.

"Malcolm was murdered because he was coming around to accepting the white man as he was and this was an assumption that threatened the existence of the Moslem movement and the whites. The Moslem movement is based on the separation of the black and white races. For the blacks to accept the whites would mean the extinction of the Moslem movement.

"The white man in America lives on the flat assumption that his morality comes directly from God. If God would tell the whites to accept the blacks, white America might accede. But God hasn't spoken. The white population fears a collapse of its morality if it accepts the blacks. It really and truly believes that God meant the separation to be. No rational argument has ever been strong enough to break this belief. And today you'll find more people taking support from this argument than in the 1860's. The white American has never been able to trust his own morality. The hatred of the blacks is the firm stand which whites can take in confidence, for to hate the blacks is morally correct until God ends the separation. It is insane. It is irrational. It is a solemn delusion. But it is the truest and most obvious fact of life in America.

"For Malcolm to announce that he accepted the whites meant he was accepting white America for what it is, and white America doesn't want to be accepted for what it is. We have managed to hide our moral history with more skill than any other nation in human history. We want to be accepted for what we are not, which is why no one in this country can ever get ten seconds of respite. We live in perpetual fear of who we are. Malcolm came as close as any black man in white American history to destroying this solemn delusion. This was because Malcolm somehow had in his own experiences the history of America. He went from the lonely individual to the corporation to the solemn lie. Malcolm finally knew truth was useless. And for a black man to state this

230

on the world level that Malcolm had access to meant that he was a danger to the entire myth of American morality and he would have to be destroyed. Malcolm was a victim of the whites and the blacks, who both wanted him killed. Malcolm knew he was going to be killed. He knew this was the price he had to pay for his discovery. We have managed to destroy absolutely every black man who has ever tried to force his identity on us as an individual man. Some are murdered like Malcolm, most die more slowly. The Negro middle class knows this, which is why they still remain silent. Emerson sees this with the same kind of dazzling clarity that led him to flee Yale, which is why Emerson wants to make the first move. Malcolm died when he gave up his victim."

I made my own notation on what West said: West is right. The whole Negro race in America has been murdered, not one single Negro has been permitted to escape. Emerson wants to be that one person. If one person can get through, then others can follow. All the others.

Whenever I left the office to meet Emerson, I felt I was starting out on the longest journey an American could make. Emerson was waiting for me now on 116th Street in the bar where he had asked me, "Did West ever give you any letters of mine to read?" I had lied. But then I had a reason for lying. West was still alive. Now I didn't know what I would do if Emerson asked me for the letters. With West dead, the letters were in my possession, either an inheritance or an obligation from West.

I left the office, which was now more of a sanctuary to me than a place to work. Everyone I knew now felt he had to have a sanctuary. Jenny Beal had come to New York for two days from Alabama. The first thing she asked me about was the eulogy. She said she would have flown in for the funeral if she had known Emerson was going to speak. She said she didn't want to see West buried by the rules of his Episcopal family. Jenny told me she had come to New York to take a black baby back to Alabama with her. "If we can adopt Korean and Chinese babies, we should certainly be able to adopt black babies. That's why I came to New York. I'm taking a black baby back to Alabama with me. I can't think of anything else to do."

I crossed Fifth Avenue to get over to the Eighth Avenue subway. Sometimes the subway has a thundering solitude.

Emerson knew I had his letters. In my conversations I must have repeated sentences from his letters. I must have been quoting him for weeks without realizing it. It was so easy to quote from Emerson's letters to West. It became impossible for me to read *The New York Times* without referring to Emerson's letters as a way of feeling out the truth of the people who were news. Whole paragraphs would come to me from his letters. "What then is our relation to one another, great White-friend, for we do have a relation. Is it to be father-son? Is it to be a dialogue, with you and me continually asking questions that would stagger the belief of a saner civilization? Are we to spend insane afternoons on East 48th Street over oak tables with heavy linen napkins resting on our laps and you asking me questions about Martin Luther King, demonstrations, Federal legislation, the University of Chicago papers on Negroes—what are we to discuss in the artificial darkness of East 48th Street? Are we always to speak as debaters? What should be the proper relationship of a black man to a white man?"

In what saner civilization? I asked myself as I went into the Eighth Avenue subway. The subway seemed to speed faster as we rushed toward Harlem. I looked up to see a Negro man who must have been over eighty years old staring at four white children and four black children who were sitting together. They didn't yell, scream, didn't fight, didn't rip the seats, didn't look as though their heads had been smashed open against brick walls. The eighty-year-old Negro man stared at the children as though some ancient ancestral dream of his had suddenly been realized on a New York subway train. That a black child and a white child could actually sit together simply as children. His eyes were the deepest wells of blackness I had ever seen. All the black history that he must have carried secretly in him for over eighty years came swimming out into his eyes.

Looking at him, I tried to imagine Emerson at the age of fifty or seventy or eighty or at his death with the file case of American history stretched out in front of him for his shroud. De Tocqueville said that the blacks and the whites in America would never meet, he said the closer the confrontation as in the North, the greater the hate; this was his vision. We all live strangely frightened of one another. This is the strangest thing about color in America, blackness itself isn't frightening, what is frightening to us is the fear of finding ourselves surrounded by people we finally have to recognize as human. We fear humanity more than anything else we have feared in our history.

From Boston, where he had gone the day after the funeral, Emerson sent me a note saying, "I ran into the only other black boy I really knew at Exeter. Now he's out of Princeton and he sits around Boston. He told me about a gang of black boys that he ran into in Boston who study the street maps of Boston, the public-utility maps, trying to figure out how to blow up the utility lines in the white neighborhoods. He told me that he wrote his Master's thesis on black religion. Then he started to shout at me as though I wouldn't listen or believe him if he spoke quietly, and he shouted, 'The white missionaries coming from Boston, this ugly city of Boston, those white missionaries taught the black slaves in the South that God meant them to be slaves and that they would get their reward in the world to come. This was beautiful for the plantation owners! The white missionaries coming from this ugly city of Boston made it everlastingly clear to the black slaves that they were a little less than human but with enough of a difference for them not to be human and they shouldn't think of themselves as being human. The slaves believed this because they thought God believed this. We let some little old ladies from Boston swallow us up! There isn't a black man alive in America today who isn't hung up on what those Boston ladies did in the South over 130 years ago.' Brooks, what was in the scream that killed S. T. West? What kind of primordial sound was it? How do we track it down? Did Mrs. Mills want to kill West? I think I've heard that scream all of my life without knowing it could kill."

I saw Emerson standing in front of the bar on 116th Street before he saw me. He wore the black suit he had worn the day he delivered West's eulogy. He looked older. There was no more youth in his face, if there had ever been. He seemed to be staring in awe at 116th Street, at the two police cars rushing away from 116th Street, the street which he said had been ugly when the blacks inherited it from the fleeing whites and was still ugly after fifty years of possession.

"It's real," Emerson said when I came up to him, "every time I look at it I have to convince myself that it's real. Those police cars you saw pulling away so fast took away a fifteen-year-old girl. I saw her come screaming out of the building on the corner. She screamed out that she had killed her baby. She said she'd smashed her baby's face with a frying pan. The police rushed into her room and found a cast-iron frying pan covered with blood. But they couldn't find the baby. Where's the baby? they shouted at her on the sidewalk. I thought the crowd was going to tear the police to pieces. By this time the girl was mute. Her screaming had stopped. Then even the police were embarrassed by her. She suddenly looked like a little girl. What the hell was she doing alone on 116th Street with a five-month-old baby? Who let her take the baby out of the hospital? C'mon," Emerson said, "let's walk. Let's go over to Morningside Park."

Morningside Park lay at the end of 116th Street, at the bottom of Columbia University, the park Columbia

University warned its students and faculty not to enter day or night. We started to climb the hill up to Morningside Heights. It was a steep hill, even with the stairway. I was sweating when we got to the top of the hill and Morningside Heights. Emerson was quiet as we climbed up the hill. Too quiet. Near the top of the hill he said, "The police couldn't find the baby. They're knocking on everybody's door asking them if they've seen a dead baby. The police are checking out the incinerators and garbage cans. When I was six years old," Emerson said, "I said to my mother, Does God answer all questions with silence?"

The sky was turning into a black gray, the clouds sweeping across the black roofs of Harlem. We could see the police cars cruising up and down the streets. The sirens didn't end.

"I went to Cleveland for three days to see my sister," Emerson said. "I wanted to see all of my family again. My sister's not pregnant yet and she never will be. She's afraid to have a black baby, even in her $50,000 house. I spent a week with my mother and father in Baltimore. They still have the oak table my father bought for $12 at the Salvation Army store. My father asked me the same question you asked, What are you going to do? He didn't say I should go into the post office, as he used to say before I went to Harvard. My mother asked me if West had left me any money. She thought I should go back to divinity school. She gave me the Bible she's been reading for the past forty years and that I actually learned to read from. The first sentence I ever read was the first sentence of Genesis." Emerson asked me, "Do you remember that eighteen-year-old that I went looking for? The police shot him in the back of his head two days ago. He was running away from a parked car with a suitcase. He had my name in his wallet and the police asked me what I knew about him. How could I tell them? What will the fifteen-year-old who smashed her baby's face say to the doctors when they ask her why she smashed her baby's face? What can any of us say any more that doesn't immediately make us feel like all the words we know are dead?"

Emerson moved away from the stone enclosure. He turned toward the Cathedral of St. John the Divine and said, "It's usually empty, very empty. Let's take a look at it." The Cathedral of St. John the Divine looked down on Harlem, a great gray hulking cathedral that nobody believes exists in New York City. How could the third-largest cathedral in Christendom exist right here in New York City? St. John the Divine lay on top of the hill that made a valley out of Harlem. It could send its angels out to fight in the valley, but it didn't.

Emerson led the way. We started for St. John the Divine almost like two pilgrims. Up from the stone enclosure, past the towering buildings of Columbia University, past the monumental façade of St. Luke's Hospital, and there, rising out of the ground, was the Cathedral of St. John the Divine, vast and gray, under construction for the past seventy-five years, still unfinished and if it was ever finished it would be the largest Gothic church in the world. But not with the awe of Chartres. That could never be. For we no longer had the same awe of life. Emerson stopped to stare at the façade of St. John the Divine. For an instant I thought he was going to turn away from the cathedral. It looked too big. Its towers were over two hundred feet high. Inside, it could hold ten thousand people. The cathedral hulked over us. I wished it could envelop us. It was enormous. Emerson seemed taken aback by its enormity. But then he moved toward the stone steps and I followed him. Emerson moved swiftly up the steps. I was behind him. Now he seemed to be rushing into the church. The police sirens echoed and echoed as we went past the great doors and into the cavernous cathedral.

The cathedral was empty. All the seats down the great aisle were empty. The stained-glass windows let through whatever light there was in the outside polluted air. The gray stone ceiling looked more real, more vast than the sky outside. Emerson touched the granite columns as though to keep the cathedral from collapsing. How could a cathedral live without people? Beyond the columns were the altar and the symbols of gold that kept one billion people from being afraid of death.

Emerson went ahead of me, toward the pulpit, passing the great American eagle that had been cast out of iron. For an instant, just an instant, but an instant as long as life itself, the life I wished for Emerson, I thought Emerson was going to mount the steps leading to the pulpit. I thought Emerson was going to fill the cathedral with his words and bring the church to life. He had his hand on the railing. Then I saw his hand stiffen. His body got taut, as frozen as the eagle cast out of iron. Then a scream broke from Emerson, a scream that tore to the ends of the cathedral, that bounded against the cold walls and that brought ministers in black frocks running toward us.

I hurried to Emerson's side. And there on the cold stone of the cathedral, hidden in the steps of the pulpit, was the baby, the dead black baby, its face smashed beyond recognition, its eyes torn out. Emerson bent down to pick up the baby. A minister said in a crazy hysterical voice, "Don't touch the baby!" Emerson didn't hear him. He held the dead baby in his arms. There were tears running down Emerson's face. He held the baby in his arms, carrying the baby like an offering, not toward the altar, but up the great aisle of St. John the Divine. "St. John!" Emerson called out. A cold chill went through me as Emerson called out again, "St. John! St. John!" The ministers didn't try to stop Emerson. They were behind him, alongside him. They stared at the dead baby. The baby was naked. Its black skin was torn as though a rat had dug its teeth into the stomach of the baby. Emerson was halfway up the aisle when a minister said to him, "Where are you taking the baby! Put the baby down! The police have to see it!" Emerson didn't answer the minister. He pushed past the minister. Emerson pushed ahead of all of us. He carried the baby past the doors of St. John the Divine. In the sunlight the streets looked insane. The buildings looked as though they had been put up by madmen. Emerson was at the top of the steps. He brought the baby up to his chest. He kissed the baby's smashed face and then he flung the baby into the street, the baby rushing over the steps in its last flight, its last moment in the sun, from its last human embrace. The ministers rushed down the stone steps toward the baby. The police sirens were already howling.

THERE HAD TO BE A VICTIM. S. T. West had known it. Now I had to believe it. Emerson found his victim.

Emerson finally committed the murder S. T. West said he would commit.

At the cocktail party S. T. West said America needed a murder, a murder that would threaten all of us, that would alert all of us at the same time, a murder to accomplish what could never be accomplished by law or logic. A murder to end the solemn delusion, the insane, irrational separation of races in America, a separation so absolute that white America murdered every black man who tried to end the separation. Not once in all of American history had a single black man been permitted to bridge the separation, to come out of the void America created. West said that "Emerson sees this with the same kind of dazzling clarity that led him to flee Yale, which is why Emerson wants to make the first move." How right West was, even though he was helpless to act himself.

Emerson said that when a man is unknown to himself, when no one can grasp him, when everything eludes him

except the certainty of his own existence, then he is nothing. "This is the condition of most men before their real
creation," Emerson said, "the creation of themselves and
what they can do on earth as men. The time of this nothingness is chaos, we all experience chaos, we all hope to
come out of the chaos, out of being nothing, to be created, to have an identity that only we can possess, that
others can recognize, that we know is ours. In this state
of nothing, black men live suspended lives, they're like
seeds with the earth on top of them, the earth never
opening up. In America," Emerson said to me, "Negro
men are forced to live this way all of the time, no root is
permitted to form, no growth to take place, no god to
intervene."

Where did Emerson find his victim in this void?

I didn't hear from Emerson until the third day after
we left St. John the Divine. I was working on a Foundation grant for Emerson that would give him enough
funds to go to any divinity school he chose, a divinity
school where he could go even further and further into
the void and then emerge out of it, forever, with his own
identity. I would never forget his Dear White Man With
No Ears letter.

Nor the inexorable letter that now arrived on my desk,
the letter that told me Emerson had finally found his
victim.

I rushed hopelessly to Emerson's room. I arrived at the
same time as the police.

I saw Emerson seated in his chair, at his table, his head
covered with a plastic bag. There was a Bible open in

front of him on the table. The Bible was open to the Twenty-third Psalm.

I wanted to lift Emerson and carry him out of the room. I wanted to carry him through all of the streets of New York, through all of the streets of America, as he was, with the plastic bag over his head, where his identity could be seen.

The letter that came from Emerson said, "I'm going to make the longest journey anyone can make. I am going to see if God exists. If God doesn't exist, then I have just died sooner and at least with some purpose."

I didn't believe Emerson's letter! It was the only letter he wrote I didn't believe. Emerson was the last person on earth to have to die to see if God exists. The existence of God doesn't require proof. But the existence of man does. This is where we stand now in the western world. We have to prove our existence to one another.

Emerson murdered himself to prove that he existed. He murdered himself to save us from being his murderers.

S. T. West said, We're all like that Roman emperor, all of us, when it comes to color, we all wish the black people in America had one neck so that we could get rid of them with a single blow of a sword.

God save all of us.

Julius Horwitz

Born in Cleveland, Ohio, in 1920, Julius Horwitz attended Ohio State and Columbia Universities and is a graduate of The New School for Social Research. His first book, *The City* (1953), was praised by critics as one of the finest books ever written about New York, and his first novel, *The Inhabitants* (1960), is read and studied in universities throughout the country for its revelations about the world of public welfare. His most recent book, *Can I Get There by Candlelight* (1964), is a novel of wartime London. Mr. Horwitz's articles on social problems in *The New York Times Magazine* and *Look* have attracted wide attention, and he has served as consultant to the Majority Leader of the New York Senate on problems of social welfare, and to the New York State Joint Legislative Committee on the Problems of Public Health and Medicare.